NO TIME FOR GLORY

Stories of World War II

illustrated by William R. Lohse

NO TIME FOR GLORY

Stories of World War II

selected by

Phyllis R. Fenner

WILLIAM MORROW & COMPANY · NEW YORK

Grateful acknowledgment is made for permission to reprint the following:

"The Secret Raiders of Ploesti," by William Chamberlain, from *The Saturday Evening Post*, © 1959 by The Curtis Publishing Company. Reprinted by permission of the author and his agents, Littauer and Wilkinson.

"Pirate Off Nantucket," by James Warner Bellah, from *The Saturday Evening Post*, © 1942 by The Curtis Publishing Company. Reprinted by permission of the author and his agents, Scott Meredith Literary Agency, Inc.

"The Commandos Go In," by Bernard Glemser, from his book, *Radar Commandos*, © 1953 by Bernard Glemser. Reprinted by permission of Holt, Rinehart and Winston, Inc.

"Leave It to Wilbur," by Arch Whitehouse, from his book, *Fighters in the Sky*, © 1942, 1951, 1959 by Arch Whitehouse. Reprinted by permission of Duell, Sloane & Pearce, Inc.

"The Walls Are Breached," by P. R. Reid, from his book, *The Colditz Story*, © 1952 by P. R. Reid. Reprinted by permission of J. B. Lippincott Company.

"The Rifles of the Regiment," by Eric Knight, from *Colliers*, © 1942 by The Crowell-Collier Publishing Company. Reprinted by permission of the author's estate.

"The Immortal Harpy," by Hobert Douglas Skidmore, from *The Saturday Evening Post*, © 1944 by The Curtis Publishing Company. Reprinted by permission of the author and his agents, Constance Smith Associates.

"The Beaches of Dunkirk," by "Bartimeus," from *The Atlantic Monthly*, © 1940 by The Atlantic Monthly Company. Reprinted by permission of Paul R. Reynolds & Son.

"The Young Man from Kalgoorlie," by H. E. Bates, from his book, *There's Something in the Air*, © 1943 by Alfred A. Knopf, Inc., and reprinted with their permission.

"The Enemy," by Pearl S. Buck, from *Harper's Magazine* and from her book, *Far and Near* (The John Day Company, 1947), © 1942 by Pearl S. Buck. Reprinted by permission of Harold Ober Associates Incorporated.

Published simultaneously in the Dominion of Canada by
George J. McLeod Limited, Toronto.
Library of Congress Catalog Card Number 62-11900

Seventh Printing, March 1970

For my friend,
Anna Buck,
in appreciation
of her help
through the years.

CONTENTS

THE SECRET RAIDERS OF PLOESTI *William Chamberlain* 13

PIRATE OFF NANTUCKET *James Warner Bellah* 33

THE COMMANDOS GO IN *Bernard Glemser* 53

LEAVE IT TO WILBUR *Arch Whitehouse* 76

THE WALLS ARE BREACHED *P. R. Reid* 99

THE RIFLES OF THE REGIMENT *Eric Knight* 132

THE IMMORTAL *HARPY* *Hobert Douglas Skidmore* 138

THE BEACHES OF DUNKIRK *"Bartimeus"* 168

THE YOUNG MAN FROM KALGOORLIE *H. E. Bates* 179

THE ENEMY *Pearl S. Buck* 196

A WORLD ON FIRE

World War I (1914 to 1918) was called "a war to end wars," but in 1934 Adolf Hitler got control of Germany and annexed Austria and Czechoslovakia. The rest of the world sat by and watched until he conquered Poland in 1939. Then France and Britain became involved. Hitler's tanks knocked out the French and drove the British Army to the beaches of Dunkirk where, but for a miracle, they would have been destroyed. The long bombing of Britain began.

On December 7, 1941, "the day of infamy," with no declaration of war, Japanese planes destroyed almost our entire main fleet at Pearl Harbor and nearly all of our aircraft on the ground in the Philippines. Germany and Italy declared war on us immediately. Thus began a war lasting from 1941 to 1945, which was "the longest, fiercest, and bloodiest war we had fought since the Civil War." It was truly a war fought around the world, and few nations escaped being drawn in.

It was also a grim war, fought with machine guns and hand grenades, tanks and jeeps, heavy bombers and little Spitfire fighting planes, PT boats and submarines, destroyers and big battleships. There was no chivalry. Civilians were killed and open cities destroyed. It was no war of songs and slogans. There was literally no time for glory.

P.F.

NO TIME FOR GLORY

Stories of World War II

The Secret Raiders of Ploesti

WILLIAM CHAMBERLAIN

The official report of the Ploesti raid—for it was only a raid, although a magnificent one—is terse and factual. It makes dry reading, for official reports are not noted for their literary quality. Its gist may be given as follows:

"On 1 August, 1943, five groups of B-24 heavy bombers, flying from airfields in the vicinity of Bengasi, made a low-level attack on enemy oil installations at Ploesti, Rumania. One hundred and seventy-seven bombers were dispatched on the mission. Fifty-four failed to return. Approximately forty per cent of the cracking and refining capacity at Ploesti was destroyed. . . ."

If you dig deep enough you may learn that five Congressional Medals of Honor were earned that day for ". . . gallantry and intrepidity . . . above and beyond the call of duty. . . ." It is doubtful, however, that you will find mention of Cass Bolivar or his ship, the *Sally Lou,* or of First Lt. Claude Bearpaw. Officially, neither Claude nor Cass Bolivar was at Ploesti at all.

Not, of course, that the omission of Bearpaw from the reports bothered Claude. In the first place, he never read official reports; in the second place, since he'd been A.W.O.L. at the time, he felt that the less said about the matter, the better.

Claude was twenty-two—a tall, rangy youth with his Cherokee ancestry showing in the high cheekbones of his face and the copper-bronze cast of his skin. Back in Oklahoma his father owned more oil wells than he could count, and Claude had been going to a football college until the Air Force had lured him away to learn to fly planes. Since he was the grandson of a chief, Claude had taken to flying—and to war—as a hound dog takes to a rabbit.

It was this zeal, coupled with a happy disregard for such things as regulations, that landed Claude in the hospital, suffering from an acute overdose of flak, early in July of 1943. His squadron—he was flying medium bombers for the Northwest African Strategic Air Force at the time—had been enjoying a one-day stand-down. The inactivity had bored Claude. Instead of reasonably heading for a binge in

Constantine, as had the rest of his fellows, he had thumbed a ride up to Sicily with a neighboring squadron which was going to bomb the railroad yards at Palermo.

Coming back, they'd run into an unplotted AA battery manned by Germans whose shooting was considerably better than that of the "Eyeties." As a result, the plane in which Claude was riding had been pretty thoroughly ventilated with flak, and Claude himself had arrived home with a dozen chunks of assorted metal in parts of his anatomy.

His C.O., a rough type, had given Claude a chewing out; then he had remarked piously that it was doubtless Allah's will—and now maybe he'd get some sleep of nights—and had consigned Claude to the hospital for repairs. That had been better than three weeks ago, and now boredom was again beginning to ride Claude. He mentioned that to the man in the next bed.

"Either I get out of here or I go nuts," Claude said darkly. "As long as they were picking iron out of me with the flak clippers it wasn't so bad—at least it passed the time away. Now these monkeys say I got to stick around here for observation—whatever that is."

The man sitting on the edge of the next bed made no answer as he lighted a cigar with meticulous care. He'd been moved in here this morning, and this was the first chance Claude had had to get acquainted. A harmless, happy-looking old guy, had been Claude's first impression. A middle-sized man with mild eyes, crow-footed at the corners, and hair that was patched with gray at the temples. Most likely, Claude thought, the other was some sort of a staff wallah in here to rest his ulcers. The other had that look.

However, Claude was a person who liked to know. "What you in here for, dad?" he asked, grinning to show that there was no offense meant.

The older man gave Claude a thoughtful stare; then he took the cigar from his mouth and inspected its burning end. "Observation," he said finally.

Claude said disgustedly, "Well, that makes two of us. You know what I think? I think this here is a nut ward they got us cooped up in." He paused to tap himself moodily on the chest with a forefinger, then introduced himself. "Bearpaw, here. Claude, first loot. You got a name, dad?"

The other said, his tone indicating it was of no great consequence, "Bolivar. Captain Cass Bolivar."

"Glad to know you, cap," Claude said, his grin coming back as he put out a hand. "What they got you doing in the white man's war? Working at the base section, maybe?"

"Flying," Cass Bolivar said. "At least that's what I was doing until they shipped me here to the hospital, lieutenant."

Claude squinted at Bolivar with new interest now. "Flying, huh? You must be new out here—I ain't seen you around before."

Cass didn't answer that at once. He was thinking, How little these brash kids, just out from the States, know of what war really is. Well, it's not your job to tell them, Cass. They'll find out for themselves all too soon.

Cass Bolivar was ten years older than Claude, but measured in terms other than years, he was already an old, old man, for he had learned of war the hard way. He had his first lesson of war while he'd watched impotently as the core of the Far East Air Force had died on Clark Field in the Philippines, amid the crash of bombs and the howl of strafing fighters. That had been a little over a year and a half ago as days went; reckoned on a starker scale—the scale of heartbreak and forlorn missions against impossible odds, and running—they took eons from a man's life that he could never get back.

Not that Cass Bolivar thought of things that way—he was not an imaginative man. He just knew that after Clark Field there had been the futility of Mindanao and the Dutch islands and India. Then, finally, Egypt, where the hastily formed United States Army Middle East Air Force—later to become the 9th Air Force—was helping to beat back Rommel's Afrika Korps; then the months of war in the desert after that. There had been too few pilots and too few planes in those days; some—not many—of both were left now, but they were old and war weary far beyond their time.

Cass Bolivar was one of those. He didn't know it, but his squadron commander—himself one of the old ones—had seen and had understood too well. He'd put the thing into words in the late afternoon three days ago, after Cass had come in for a bad landing. Cass had ground-looped the *Sally Lou* in the dust of the desert field, and Bull Holliday had waited until the rest of the *Sal's* crew had moved off out of earshot before he'd given Cass the business.

"You've had it, Cass," he'd said quietly then. "I've been watching since we started practicing on this low-level strike. It's no dice. I'm sorry, but I'm pulling you off flying."

It had taken a minute for that to sink in. "You mean I'm not going on the Big One?" Cass had asked then, disbelieving.

"That's right," Bull had said in a flat, hard voice, because that was the only way. "Young Stahl will take the *Sal.* I'm sending you back for a rest. That way maybe you'll live long enough to fly again before this war is over."

Probably Bull Holliday hadn't realized that he was delivering Cass into the eager clutches of the medics, but that was the way it had worked out. Presently Cass had found himself on a C-47 consigned back to the base section. Here at the hospital this morning he'd been gleefully welcomed by a medical major named Micklejohn—a bulgy little man with a toothbrush mustache and eyes that glittered with a bird-dog look behind shiny pince-nez as he hastily scanned the papers that Cass had brought with him.

"Hah!" Micklejohn said to the medical lieutenant with him. "A perfect case of battle fatigue, Jensen—it's all here. Clearly a subconscious withdrawal from reality in the subject's actions. That ground loop, for example."

"That ground loop was because the rudder stuck," Cass had growled. The major had paid no attention.

"Put him in Ward Three, Jensen," he had said. "We've got another interesting case in there—a lieutenant who thinks he likes to fly combat missions. Got wounded over Sicily when he wasn't even supposed to be there. Screwy, eh?"

Cass, with an effort, brought his attention back to Claude. The latter, he saw, was squinting a little suspiciously while he tried to digest the fact that Cass was a flier.

"You wouldn't," Claude asked, "be one of those Air Transport boys, would you, cap? What kind of flying you been doin'?"

"Different kinds," Cass said.

"Been on any combat missions?"

"A few."

"How many?"

"After a hundred I lost count," Cass said.

Claude's jaw dropped as he stared back; then he stood up and batted Cass enthusiastically on the back. "Well, I'll be!" he said. "Let's us do a sneak out of here, cap. Any guy that's flown a hundred missions, I got to buy a drink for!"

"I could do with a drink," Cass said thoughtfully. "Don't suppose that the medicos would approve, though."

"They won't even know about it," Claude said. "I know an orderly around this dump that likes money—he'll sneak us out our clothes if I wave a few francs at him. How about it?"

Cass started to refuse—then changed his mind. What did he have to lose? "When do we go?" he asked.

Claude gave him a wide grin. "Meet me in the can in five minutes, cap," he said. "I'll have the duds with me."

He fished an oversized roll of paper money from beneath his pillow, and explained obliquely, "Got into a crap game with the Navy last night. Navy'd never heard of the Cherokee luck—it cost 'em, cap," and departed down the aisle between the beds. Cass Bolivar stared after him. Cass was beginning to like Claude Bearpaw.

Presently the two of them left the hospital unchallenged. Claude hailed a ramshackle cab and gave the Arab driver an address. Cass's old uniform felt slack and comfortable as he lighted a fresh cigar and looked at his companion through the smoke. Claude's uniform was on the informal side. He wore wrinkled khaki trousers and a khaki shirt with the sleeves chopped off above the elbows. A long-billed baseball cap was canted on the back of his head, and his pilot's wings had been pinned to the breast of his shirt upside down.

"Distress signal, cap," he explained to Cass. "Lo, the pore Injun has shore been distressed in that hospital."

"I see," Cass murmured. He was liking Claude better.

The taxi stopped before an establishment that had *Café Georgette* painted on a window. Claude hopped out, pushing a wad of paper money at the driver and beckoning to Cass. He led the way into a dim room, empty except for three sailors, sitting broke and glum at a far table, and a woman, grossly fat, who stood behind a bar.

"Set, cap," Claude commanded. "This is on me. Hey, Mamma, you remember the Injun boy from Oklahoma?"

The fat woman squinted, then smiled broadly. "Ah," she said, "it is the Lieutenant Bearfeet, no? *Allo, mon ami.*"

"Paw—not feet," Claude corrected amiably. " 'Bout the same difference though, I guess. You remember how to mix them Oklahoma Specials like I showed you last time I was here, ma'am?"

"Those drinks," Mamma said piously, "I don't forget."

"Then mix up a couple for me and the cap," Claude told her. "Come to think of it, dearie, better mix five and we'll treat those swabbies in the corner. They're our allies, sort of."

Mamma waddled out and soon returned with glasses filled with a murky-looking liquid. She placed two down on the table and carried the others to where the sailors sat. The latter accepted enthusiastically. Claude lifted his own glass. "Mud in your eye, cap," he said.

Cass sipped. His first thought was that the concoction had a flat, insipid taste; his second thought was that someone had suddenly aimed a lighted blowtorch down his gullet. He choked violently, and tears ran down his cheeks as he tried to get his breath.

"My ole grandpappy's recipe," Claude explained. "He was a Cherokee chief. After the first jolt, it goes down easier."

"Oof!" Cass said in a husky whisper. "Wha'—"

"Cognac, bay rum, dago red, and cayenne pepper," Claude explained in a matter-of-fact voice.

The second swig did go down more easily, and a warm, comfortable glow began to run through Cass. They had two more Specials, Claude dispatching refills to the grateful sailors each time. The latter had perked up and were singing now.

"You don't look like a nut to me, cap," Claude said, peeking owlishly at Cass after the third Special. "What they observin' you for, anyway? Or did you just get in the glue with some of the high brass?"

The Specials had thawed Cass's customary reserve, and presently he was telling Claude about the events that had led up to his relief from his squadron. He spoke, keeping his voice low, of a coming operation which he referred to only as the Big One; it was to be a low-level attack—for days now his group had been practicing on simulated targets laid out in the desert. Tricky business—very tricky—for a B-24 was never meant to bomb at treetop level. It was hard enough just to fly such a mission in practice; it would be hell on wheels to take such an attack in against fighters and flak.

Claude's eyes were bright with interest now. "This Big One, cap—where's it going? You know?"

Cass shook his head. "That's security stuff and I can't tell. But it'll be big and it's coming soon."

"I got a grapevine around these parts," Claude said, frowning thoughtfully. "This morning I hear that a bunch of the big brass is flying east tonight. Going to see the show, you think?"

"I wouldn't know," Cass said heavily. "I think we've got trouble coming through the door, Bearpaw."

Claude turned his head. The street entrance had opened and a bulgy major, a lieutenant at his shoulder, had just entered. The major paused for a moment, blinking his eyes behind his pince-nez to accustom them to the gloom. It was Micklejohn and his assistant, Jensen; now he stalked forward, smiling as a cat smiles at a mouse.

"I had a hunch we'd find our two flown birds here," he chortled triumphantly. "All right, you two, are you coming quietly or do we have to send for the net?"

He reached a pudgy hand for Cass Bolivar's arm. Over in the corner the three sailors had stopped singing and were watching, dark scowls on their faces. Inspiration suddenly moved Claude.

"Hey, give us a hand, Navy!" he yelled. "These are the two nuts that stole officers' uniforms and escaped from the hospital this morning! There's free beer for anybody who takes 'em back!"

Claude's grandpappy, the Cherokee chief, had dreamed up the Oklahoma Specials in order to condition young braves for the warpath. It worked about the same on the Navy. The smallest of the trio, a bullet-headed and much-tattooed man, started across the floor purposefully; his two companions followed. Major Micklejohn's eyes glittered fiercely behind his glasses as he backed away.

"We're not the lunatics!" he yelped shrilly. "We're—"

"That's what they all say," Claude said in a severe tone.

"Grab 'em, boys!" the tattooed sailor said. He lowered his head and butted the major in the belly. His mates closed in and the room was suddenly filled with salty language and flying arms and legs. Claude dumped paper money onto the table as Mamma screamed behind the bar.

"Let's get out of here, cap," Claude said practically. "Looks like the United States Navy has got the situation in hand."

He hauled Cass toward a side door, and the two of them went along a winding alley at a gallop to come presently to a wider street. Here Claude flagged down a passing cab and piled in after Cass, shouting orders to the Arab driver in pidgin English.

Cass Bolivar recovered his breath enough to ask, "Where are we going, lieutenant? Back to the hospital?"

Claude shook his head and looked at the other out of the corners of his eyes. "Be just as well if we're not around when those swabbies show up with their escaped nuts, cap," he said. "Why don't we just go to Bengasi, instead?"

Cass blinked, beginning to wonder if possibly Claude was a mental case after all. "Bengasi?" he asked blankly.

"Yup," Claude said, but the levity had gone out of his voice. "You were telling me back there, cap, about how you've been drilling the *Sal's* crew for this low-level strike—even with all that drill you figure it's going to be a rough deal, huh?"

Cass nodded. "Rough as a cob."

"O.K.," Claude agreed in a flat voice. "So I want to ask you something. You figure that copilot of yours—Stahl was his name, wasn't it?—can take the *Sal* wherever she's going and bring her back?"

Heaviness settled into Cass Bolivar's face. He knew the answer to that question; it was an answer that had kept him awake for the past two nights. Because he knew too well that young Ed Stahl had too few missions behind him to be ready for this one.

"No," he said to Claude now. "I don't think he can."

"So we go to Bengasi," Claude said, as though that clinched it. "Somebody has got to fly the *Sal,* don't they?"

Cass rubbed fingers slowly across his chin. "And you've got some idea how we can get to Bengasi, lieutenant?" he asked, wondering if he, too, were really nuts.

"Oh, shore," Claude said, his good nature returning. "Like I said, cap, I got spies around. One of 'em is at the airfield that we're headed for. Give him a few francs and he'll smuggle us onto that plane that is taking the brass up to Bengasi tonight."

"What'll the brass say to that?"

Claude flapped a hand. "Shucks, they won't even know

we're there. We'll get us some fatigues and smear grease on our pusses and make like we're along to help hold the ship together."

Claude, squatting on his heels beside the squat shape of the *Sally Lou,* shivered in the gray dawn. The desert can be cold before the sun comes up. Cass Bolivar had finished his inspection of the ship; now he stood a little apart talking with the crew chief of the *Sal*'s ground crew, a lanky sergeant who had not questioned the captain's return. Trucks were jouncing across the sand in the growing light, and Claude lounged to his feet. One of the trucks stopped a little way off and men climbed down. Cass Bolivar went to meet them.

That would be the *Sal*'s combat crew, Claude knew. They had halted to stand in a little huddle, and Claude grinned tightly as he heard the little murmur of surprise that ran through them. An incautious voice carried from the rear. "Holy smoke, it's the skipper!"

Cass Bolivar seemed not to hear, and he spoke with the tone of a man who had never been away. "Morning, men," he was saying. "Sorry to have missed the briefing. . . . You can fill me in after we get in the air, Ed. You'll ride copilot, as usual."

"Yes, sir." That would be young Stahl, Claude guessed. The kid had a high, reedy voice, and there was no mistaking the relief that was in it. "What about York, captain? He was to ride copilot."

"Sorry, York," Cass said, his voice clipped. "You won't be going on this trip, son. With the load that the *Sal*'s carrying today, there'll be no room for an extra passenger. Any other questions?"

Across the field now the morning was filled with the roar of warming engines, but here by the *Sally Lou* a pregnant silence held the crew for a moment. Then a gunner's voice broke the tension. "Me, I'm happy," he said.

Claude heard the murmur of approval that followed; then Cass Bolivar was saying, "Load up, men," and a new thought struck Claude, so that he scowled and ducked beneath a wing.

If Cass Bolivar meant to leave that extra copilot behind, it was a pretty good bet that Claude Bearpaw could get left behind, too, if he wasn't careful. Nuts to that, Claude decided, and climbed through a hatch into the *Sal*'s belly.

The *Sal* was air-borne before the tail gunner, a sergeant named Hortha, spotted Claude. Hortha's mouth dropped open a little when he saw Claude's lieutenant's bars and the wings worn upside down.

"Ain't you kind of new around here, lootenant?" Hortha asked then. "Or maybe I just got a bad memory?"

Claude grinned. "I came along for the ride."

"Cripes," Hortha grunted, "the skipper will blow his top for sure does he find we got a passenger."

"He ain't a passenger—not if he can shoot a waist gun, he ain't," a sergeant named Moss said. "Barney went sick at the briefing, and no replacement for him showed up."

"I'm murder with a machine gun," Claude said modestly.

"Murder's our business today," Moss answered dourly.

They crossed the Mediterranean, reaching for altitude,

for there were mountains ahead. The *Sal* grumped steadily along, preserving radio silence and holding her place in the low squadron of the task force. Sergeant Moss shouted to make himself heard above the pulsing roar of the Liberator's four engines.

"We're Tail-end Charley in this show," he said, and his voice sounded unhappy. "By the time we get to Ploesti, every fighter and every flak battery in Rumania will be waiting for us."

"So that's where we're going," Claude grunted. "Well, nobody dies, sergeant. I got the word."

"I hope you're right," Moss answered.

In the cockpit Cass Bolivar sat relaxed, the joy of flying in him and his mind tight on the job ahead. In the right-hand seat young Ed Stahl, copilot, fidgeted nervously. "I'm glad they let you come along, captain," he said.

"They didn't," Cass told him. "Don't ask questions."

The time paddle-footed away. Below, mountains slipped into the leading edges of the *Sal*'s wings, were spewed out behind. Ahead, the ships of another squadron made black bugs against the sky. Cass spoke into the interphone, nodded curtly at his navigator's reply. They'd be heading down for the deck soon.

The altimeter was winding down now, and the mountains were lost astern as they dropped into the valley of the Danube. They fled over fields where peasants watched; startled faces turned up as the bomber stream roared on. The broad reaches of the Danube were left behind; ahead, and still far away, black smoke was beginning to climb into the summer sky. The first of the raiders had already struck. It was scant minutes later when Cass spotted the German fighters—ME-109's coming in head on and fast.

Thank God, Cass's mind said with detached calm, we're low. They can't get at us so well down here—

The interphone had suddenly come alive, and, still with that detachment, Cass's mind fitted the snatches of words into a pattern which told him of the battle that raged around the *Sal* now. Nothing he could do about it. He had his own hands full with the heavy ship as it bucked in the tricky air currents coming off the ground below. The voices pulsed on in his ears.

"Three fighters coming in at nine o'clock high. . . . Roger. . . . Nose gunner to left waist. . . . ME one-oh-nine coming down your side close. . . . I'm awaitin' for him, boy. . . ."

The last voice had belonged to Claude Bearpaw, Cass realized without any particular surprise. He could have guessed that; one way or another Claude would have come along on this trip. The *Sal* shuddered with the rack of the fifty calibers—all guns going except those in the ball turret in her belly.

The voice of the gunner there reached Cass with a Texas-accented lament. "I cain't see nothin' down heah for all the trees hittin' me in the face."

Ahead, the smoke column—shot with scarlet—climbed higher into the sky; it was racing closer with giant strides. Off to one side a Liberator fell off on one wing—dived suddenly into the ground to explode in a great gout of flame. Far ahead, two more Liberators went down. It was getting harder to hold the *Sal*; Cass jabbed the button of his mike and yelled at Ed Stahl, who was hunched in the right-hand seat, his face the color of dirty canvas.

"Help me hold her! Once we hit those updrafts over the target, she'll buck like a steer!"

No answer came back from the copilot. Cass glanced quickly; saw the shattered side window and the spreading dark stain and the red froth on Stahl's lips. Young Ed Stahl had bought it.

No time for that now—time was running out and the target just ahead. A boiling caldron of smoke and flame, which seethed with the violence of a volcano. The ships of the group ahead were gulped up by the smoke as Cass tried to spot the landmarks that would guide him to the cracking plant which was the *Sal's* target. No good. The whole world was going up in flame, and there was nothing to see. The *Sal* ran on, exploding flak swaddling her on all sides now. A thump smashed like a giant fist against the fuselage beneath Cass, and fragments of red-hot iron bit at his legs.

He pushed the mike button again. "Pilot to bombardier—we won't be able to find our primary in this—toggle on any target you can see." The reply seemed faint and far away as it came back. "Bombardier to pilot—Roger—good luck, skipper."

Just before the smoke swallowed them, Cass saw a great chunk of metal peel back from the *Sal's* nose and go kiting away. The ship seemed to have gone wild now; it was being flung about like a leaf in a gale. Across the way, Ed Stahl's head lolled loosely on his shoulders as the *Sal* pitched and yawed. The acrid smell of burning oil seeped into the cockpit to sting Cass's nostrils and burn his eyes.

He felt a shudder run through the ship, and then the bombardier's voice came again over the interphone. "Bombs away." The *Sal* surged upward, free of her load, and a spark of exultation warmed Cass for a moment. We're going to make it, he thought. By gosh, we're going to make it! The smoke had started to thin when he saw a black flower, wearing a scarlet core at its center, blossom ahead and a little below. A white-hot spear rammed into Cass's side, and he felt his fingers go numb on the controls.

You've bought it, Cass, his mind said fuzzily. Who is going to take the *Sal* back now?

In the last seconds of consciousness left to him, Cass Bolivar had his answer. A rangy youth, wearing a khaki shirt with the sleeves chopped off above the elbows and wings pinned on upside down, was hauling Ed Stahl out of his seat.

"Move over, bud," Claude Bearpaw was saying crazily. "Let papa drive this here chariot."

Cass Bolivar felt good as the last of the daylight went.

Afterward, when he would think of it, the details of the rest of that day were never too clear to Claude. He did things, but memory of doing them would never come to a sharp, clear focus in his mind. It was like a picture seen in a kaleidoscope.

Sergeant Moss, dead and lying among the empty fifty-caliber cartridge cases beneath his gun. Turret gunner dead, and bombardier dying. Young Ed Stahl hit in the chest. Cass Bolivar hit bad, too, and the navigator—blood running down the side of his own face—giving rough first aid back on the deck. That was the way it went as Claude fought the bucking ship.

The fighters came in again as they left the funeral pyre of Ploesti behind. Now the *Sal* no longer had the covering fire of other ships to protect her as she lumbered back across the valley—most of her own guns were silent now. An exploding 20-mm. shell drove hot chards into Claude's thigh, but he didn't notice as—his face set into granite lines—he held the *Sal* close to the ground, zigzagging a course across the fields. Vaguely he noted that the *Sal*'s black shadow ran with them like a great bird below.

He thought vaguely, You get out of this one, boy, and you can shore say "thank you" to the Man Upstairs.

It was a long while later when they came to the mountains again, the *Sal* limping on three engines now. Claude fought for altitude; somehow they made it with nothing to spare. More eons drifted by, and then the blue of the Mediterranean showed ahead. The navigator came to crouch at Claude's back.

"We're losing gas," the navigator said in a toneless voice. "We can't make it back to base."

Claude scowled through the streaks that sweat had cut across the smoke-grimed mask of his face. The leg of his khaki trousers was dark with blood, he noticed without emotion.

"Then we'll ditch," he said.

"I'll have the wounded ready," the navigator said, without comment. "There's only five of us left."

"Roger," Claude told him tiredly.

There were other events after that—hazy things not well

remembered. The sound as the *Sal* settled into the water, and the sound, seconds later, as the *Sal* died. The yellow life raft bobbing on the choppy sea and, after a long, long while, the sharp, clean lines of the destroyer coming toward them.

"Always figured the Navy was our allies," Claude mumbled a little crazily. "Buy 'em all an Oklahoma Special sometime."

Back in the hospital Claude and Cass Bolivar again had beds that were side by side. Cass lay quietly, propped up and cigar clamped in a corner of his mouth; restlessness was already beginning to ride Claude again. An orderly came down the aisle between the beds.

"Hey," Claude said heartily, "if it ain't Fingers Moody, the guy that likes money. How you be, chum?"

The orderly approached warily. "What you want now, lootenant?" he asked. "Whatever it is, I ain't got it."

"Jest a little information, son," Claude told him, fishing money from beneath his pillow. "Maybe you could tell us what happened to that major in the pinch-nose glasses that used to be around here."

The orderly glanced over his shoulder—then grinned. "You mean Major Micklejohn, lootenant? They got him and Lootenant Jensen over in Ward Four. It seems they got took with battle fatigue. Say, what did you two guys do after I brung you your clothes, anyway?"

Claude considered the question for a long moment. When he finally answered, his reply made even the terse official reports sound like the grossest kind of overstatement.

"A bunch of us went up to Ploesti," Claude said. "Some of us came back. That was about all there was to it."

Pirate off Nantucket

JAMES WARNER BELLAH

Andy Cassat ate his supper in sullen silence. The algebra books lay under the lamp on the red-and-white-checked cloth. Mrs. Albro would tell him to get at them as soon as he finished. That's what his brother paid her for—to cook and clean and sew and keep the house for Andy to study in and live in.

"I'm goin' to tell your brother where you were again this afternoon, soon's he docks," she said. Andy put his fork down. "He ain't goin' to like it"—the thin lips snapped shut

—"because your job's to stay in school, not to hang around that Navy recruitin' fella at the post office."

"I wasn't hangin' around," Andy said angrily. "I was talking to him 'bout enlistin' in the inactive reserve—I can graduate and still be called up next fall—when I'm seventeen. And after I'm in, maybe I can go to Annapolis."

The woman shook her head. "Michael Cassat ain't goin' to allow it. I've heard him talk to you about gettin' yourself educated. You ain't enlistin' in the Navy. I mind the night he took you up to the graveyard and showed you them family gravestones. He couldn't get an education like your old people had, so he had to go for a common sailor himself. But you ain't goin' for one, so get it out of your mind."

"He didn't do so bad," Andy growled. "He's got his master's ticket; he'll be going as captain next trip or the one after. Cap'n Whitehouse's a sick man. He knows it and Mike knows it. Likely, Mike'll have the *Bannockburn* herself—one of the smaller boats anyway."

"It took him a good many years," Mrs. Albro said, "making up for the lack of the book learning he's giving you. Don't think he's going to forget that. And he's mighty stubborn, is your brother Michael. You git after those schoolbooks now."

"Not till I hear the news." Andy swung around in his chair and snapped on the radio switch. ". . . rich, creamy lather . . . the fourth vessel to send out its distress call since dawn yesterday, when the *Languedoc* was attacked. Authoritative naval sources believe that there are at least two enemy raiders operating in the waters of the Boston coastal area. No further details are available at the present time."

"Is that so?" Andy snorted at the radio. He reached for a rolled chart on the shelf above. "That's all you know about it. There doesn't have to be but one sub!" He spread the chart out on the table. "I bet I can put my finger almost on the spot that fourth ship went down—if I knew the ship, where she was going or coming from. On a twenty-mile segment of a circle—not knowing it. What do you want to bet?"

"I ain't bettin'," said Mrs. Albro firmly, "and you git to studyin' now."

"You look here," Andy said. "I bet I could tell them in Boston it only has to be one submarine. I bet it's so obvious they haven't thought of it. She's intercepting whatever is taking a departure from the lightship or making a landfall on her."

Mrs. Albro watched his flushed, excited face. It always hurt her to see him that way, because that way he looked just as her own Eddie would have looked. She pressed her lips tightly together in faint remembered pain.

Andy pointed a finger at her. "She's run away from two areas. So they take it for granted she'll run away from the third. But this time she fools 'em. She just moves off her course a little, submerges and lies on the shelf until sundown again. Sundown today. And I'll bet she's lying between a southeasterly bearing from the lightship and say a shade just east by south. That way whatever comes in from South Africa, or leaves New York for Europe, or comes in from—"

Mrs. Albro looked at him.

"—Bermuda," Andy said. He stared at the chart for a moment. "It's too soon for Mike." His voice was sharp, for he suddenly realized that it wasn't too soon. A quick run down, a quick unloading and a quick run back, and Mike could be docking in Boston.

He twisted the radio again. "Survivors of the *Languedoc* and the *Choctaw* were brought into Boston late this afternoon. So far, it is known that there are seven survivors of the *Pitcairn Island* aboard an unspecified Coast Guard cutter still at sea, but no further word has been received from the *Bannockburn* since she sent out her distress—"

"Mrs. Albro, it's the *Bannockburn!*" He was turned toward her, white-faced, staring at the woman, his eyes stinging at the corners, so that for a second he could hardly see her. Then he grabbed up his chart and his cap, and barged out of the house. A dog was barking in the quietude of the supper hour.

The night was drawn down tightly around him and around the whole island, and somewhere in that darkness his old people stood with him. He felt them suddenly as Mike felt them. The compulsion of them. The obligation to them. Old whaling masters and old clipper captains in their white knee breeches and their gold-headed ebony canes. Dead Cassats come back from the cities of the world and the lanes of the seven seas to sleep on Nantucket. Captain Makepeace Cassat, of the *Orion.* Captain Rufus Cassat, of the barkentine *Nora.* And suddenly all that his brother Mike had ever told him was a blinding consciousness in his mind.

"Your old people aren't ever going to let you go, Andy. You'll know, when you get older. Because they're you and you're them. So get a grip on them at the start, and make 'em work for you. Make your life out of what they gave you, good blood and bad. Drink, devil, and duty, but do the job! And remember always it's the little things that make the job. Remember the little things and you'll never have to worry about the big ones. Because that's what the big things always are—the sum of the little ones."

His brother Mike was almost old enough to be his father, and all Andy's life he tried to be. But he was cold about it sometimes, harsh about it, ruthless.

Andy was tearing toward Jessup's now, through the narrow streets of the old town, his breathing deep and strong within his young chest, and his leg muscles hard to the impact of his feet on the roadway. He burst into the lighted store and turned around deliberately to close the door and steady himself. The air inside was warm and heavy with the smell of salt fish and new rubber boots and tub butter and kerosene.

"Just heard it, Andy," Owen Jessup said. "It said they picked up the call at about ten minutes of five—no position, no nothing else. That's two hours ago. They'll have sent destroyers out, and planes. It's tough on Mike." Owen passed his rough hand across his mouth and shook his head.

"Owen"—Andy Cassat walked over and put both hands flat on the worn counter—"I want the *Sally J.*"

"Aw, say now, Andy; Mike wouldn't want this himself. It's crazy. They'll do everything possible out of Boston. If you think a minute, you'll know that. Even *they* haven't got the *Bannockburn*'s last position. You can't just shove off in sixty feet and comb around the whole ocean."

"That's not what I'm going to do. And it isn't the whole

ocean." And Andy spread out his chart on the counter and put his finger under Nantucket Lightship. "Owen, you've got to believe me. Give me your parallel rule. Here. Like this." Andy worked for a minute laying off bearings. "I know it, Owen. That sub wouldn't head farther south, because she's working the lightship. Everything she's done so far proves it. Mike says they always work the lightships, and a man's a fool to use them in wartime. That's how I know that the same sub got Mike, and where it got him. It was swinging on this circle." He swung the circle with Owen's navigator's compass, a continuation of the circle that intercepted the positions of the *Choctaw* and the *Pitcairn Island* attacks. "And they got Mike right in here. Well off the lightship, but on that same circle. They got him by chance! The sub just kept swinging on that circle—and it caught Mike. I want to go out there in the *Sally J* right away."

Owen looked at him. "You know you're right, Andy, don't you?"

"Sure as I'm standing here!"

"Get going then; I'll meet you on the *Sally*. Get Black Oke."

Andy headed for the dead-end alleyway behind Carson's shop and pounded on Black Oke's door.

Fifteen minutes later they were swaying up the *Sally*'s heads'ls to get way on her to cast off.

At the outer harbor buoy, Owen nodded to Andy. "You keep her."

"I'm laying for Great Point in a minute."

"Right." Owen shouted forward, "On the jib sheets, Oke!"

It was just on to ten when they came up on Great Point Light and beat around the point laying for Sankaty Head. Owen took the wheel and Andy turned in.

Somewhere not so many miles away, Mike was in those same waters. Maybe he was in a boat, rowing. Maybe he was alone, swimming in his belt, pushing a piece of timber along with him. Big, vital Mike. Or maybe—Andy closed his eyes tightly and clenched his fists—he was just in them, floating face downward.

The nervous excitement washed out of his youth and he slept until Black Oke and Owen came about again and rolled him out of the bunk.

It was five o'clock. Owen put a flashlight down to the chart he had spread on the cockpit deck and pointed. "We're just about in here, Andy. Here's where your last tick is. Over there is Nantucket."

"You're way south; you must have had wind."

Owen nodded. "We've been footing it pretty steadily all night. Now I figure we'll run off another three quarters of an hour as we go, and come about again. That'll put us just north of your ticked position. Then if the wind holds, we'll run it out until noon. If we don't find anything by noon, we'll come in and call it a sail."

Andy looked at him for a moment. "That's it, Owen, because we haven't got a radio set, so we can't know what the Navy's found. But if they didn't find anything, and we don't, we'll know then that there isn't anything."

"Don't talk like that. We came out to get Mike. So we get Mike."

The three of them lapsed into the silence of night sailing,

waiting for the dawn to whiten to port. Suddenly they could see the tight line of the *Sally*'s backstay against the darkness above and the lower course of reef points and her slapping lazy jacks, and that was the beginning of dawn.

"Owen!" Andy exclaimed.

At the wheel, Black Oke stared in surprise.

Three hundred yards to starboard there was a black can buoy, only larger—and it wasn't a can buoy. There were men beside it—standing beside it, and a head over top of it, and a voice, "On the schooner! Heave to—at once!"

"For God's sake, head up, Oke!" Owen breathed through his teeth. Black Oke didn't need the word; he was throwing the wheel as soon as Owen started to speak.

"Hold her!" the voice bellowed at them across the water. "What ship?"

"*Sally J*, out of Nantucket."

"Stand by for boarding. You're a prize. Muster all hands on deck by your wheel. I'm coming along your starboard side. Hold her up as she goes." And they saw the machine gun on her bridge rail, trained on them.

In the half-light, all of it was completely unreal—all of it but that voice. The three of them stood rigid in the *Sally*'s cockpit, with bitter saliva threading down the backs of their throats and the bend of their elbows cold with nerve tension.

The submarine turned slowly toward them, rounded behind, and they could smell the hot uncleanliness of heavy diesel smoke.

Owen reached out for Andy's arm and bit into it with his fingers. "Son, you ain't talked yet. When you do, be careful."

"You didn't have to say that."

Close to, it was an unholy craft. Lean, metallic, vicious. A trespasser and a murderer with the blood of four ships on her. And the sudden hatred in the boy was pain for a moment. Blind hatred that Owen had seen in his eyes.

There were four men forward of the submarine's conning tower. The wet-gun crew. Damp-looking, rumpled men in sea boots and sweaters watching the lightening waters to the northward and eastward like hunted animals, their backs to the *Sally*. All of the blackness of the raider was white-streaked and weathered gray. Sea-worn, softened. And suddenly the three men on the *Sally* saw something more. She was torn up, ripped ragged, between the wet gun and the conning tower. The edges of the rip were a jagged blossoming of torn steel.

"Sumpin' done hit her," Black Oke breathed.

Owen nodded.

And again the voice on her hailed them, "Steady!" They could see her officer's face now under the visor of his cap, tight drawn along the jaw lines, young—hard young. He had his hands on the wet wheel, laying his ship alongside, himself. Deep bells rang inside of her and white water boiled in her wake. She came in on the *Sally* neatly, rubbing her, holding close to her and stopping. The gun-access trunk hatch opened and more men came up out of her, men with white faces and white hands under the dirt. Sick white from no sunlight.

The rip in her topsides had opened great torn leaves of her deck plates about eight feet forward of the base of her conning tower, ruffled them upward and outward and cut in below into the hull itself, for inside the tear there was growling green flame suddenly, a portable oxy torch, and the movement of men in small space. And as one man moved there was white paint visible far beyond the hole and the glare of electric lights from below. Not a direct hit, because that would have penetrated her and blown her open, but a close-in lashing, with the shell splinters ripping her wet superstructure wide and cutting through it to hull her. The 4.7's on the *Bannockburn.*

The broad sheer of the *Sally* ground against the rounded submerged side of the submarine, and the boarding party took short runs and leaped to the schooner's deck, awkwardly, as if their legs were stiff. The boarding officer had a long-snouted automatic pistol in his hand with a black leather lanyard across the shoulder of his gray sweater. He steadied himself and stepped down into the cockpit. He was extremely young, and arrogant in his youth.

He jerked his head toward Andy and Owen and Black Oke. Ridiculously and momentarily, as if he had read in a book that he must do just that. He said, "Leutnant zur See Hessels," and thereafter he ignored them completely, except to look at them now and then. He searched the cabin and the forepeak, and sent a man to the main masthead. Lines coiled off the raider and struck on the *Sally*'s deck with a bony rattle, and in a few moments she was hauled in close to the submarine.

The skipper shouted in German to Hessels, and the boarding party tried to lay the *Sally*'s main and fores'l booms across the submarine's deck, but both boats were still up into the wind and the schooner's canvas was backed. They couldn't walk the booms, even outboard of the *Sally.*

They hitched lines to the boom ends and hauled from the submarine's deck. That way they got the booms outboard, but it didn't please the officer on the conning tower.

It was thirteen hours since the *Bannockburn* had sent out her call. If there had been a chance, it was going. If Mike was only there alone, he was on his own now, with the *Sally* caught, with only the new day to give him hope. Big, blustering Mike. Andy wanted to cry, not actual tears, but deep inside of him, because no matter what happened now, it wouldn't be any good if Mike was gone. What in heck are they after? What are they trying to do? he thought.

The raider's skipper was bellowing at Hessels, and Hessels, on the *Sally,* was standing stiffly to attention. He said, "Yes, Herr Kapitän," twice, and he yelled angrily at his men. It wasn't arrogance with Hessels. It was sullenness. The heavy, controlled sullenness of insufficiency and fear. He lived with fear and he was worn by it. Fear had stolen his youth.

Then Owen was getting it. Black Oke was getting it. They all got it suddenly together.

Andy stood up and moved close to Owen. "She can't submerge, and dawn's caught her, so she's going to use us as a decoy, with our canvas to blanket her and our shadow to lie in when the sun comes up."

"Maybe," Owen growled, "but they ain't sailors. Not a sailor in the lot."

"Owen, she can't stay out here, even with us. She's safe enough from the north'ard because of Nantucket. That's why she's on our starboard side. But she'll have to run farther inshore, farther east with us. You watch."

Owen nodded. "That's sensible. It wouldn't be No Man's, would it?"

"You've got it. Fifty-five miles, and the further inshore she gets, the less chance of a destroyer spotting her."

"No one but the caretaker on No Man's to bother with," Black Oke whispered. "Sho, sho, No Man's. 'At's it. To refit and repair."

"You vill not shpeak togedder!" They all turned quickly. Hessels, gun in hand, was glaring at them.

"Even if I can tell you how to do what you are trying to do?" Andy said.

"Iss no madder!" Hessels shouted at him. "Keep shtill!"

"Can I tell him?" Andy pointed at the skipper. His voice was soft, almost eager.

Owen stared as if the boy had struck him. His eyes went blank, cold; Black Oke's eyes were wide in disbelief.

"What are you trying to do, help him?" Owen growled.

"Silenz!" Hessels brought the gun up slowly.

From the conning tower, the captain called across in German. Hessels answered him.

"On the schooner! You will not talk!" the German said. "You, boy, there at the wheel. Do you hear me?"

"You've got to get yourself lower in the water," Andy said.

Now, you can't hit anything you shoot at from the hip. But Hessels did. He jerked his wrist and pulled the trigger of his automatic with quick fury, jerked the trigger with his wrist bent. The heavy explosion tore the loose expanse of the early morning like a knife, cutting through taut fabric. Hessles' action was so blindly the action of an infuriated, half-frightened boy that the sound of the shot sobered him at once and stopped him from firing again. A bitter whiff of burned powder swept into Black Oke's broad nostrils. His knees began to give, and his big, hunched body turned slowly as he went down with the dawn light gleaming on his great white teeth and his enormous, surprised eyeballs. Then he pitched heavily onto the deck planking and lay on his back, his hands to his belt line. The shot had taken him vitally. Oke lay there looking up at Andy and Owen, telling them with his eyes.

Then he told Hessels with his voice, "You done killed me, white boy, foh no reason," and quite simply Black Oke died. So simply that it was the most terrible thing that would ever happen.

There was Black Oke that they had known all their lives. Only it wasn't Black Oke; it was a dreadful, outraged, dead reminder of Black Oke. And there were Owen Jessup's eyes, telling Andy why forever.

The voice on the conning tower ignored all of it blandly. "Why do I have to get lower in the water?" it said.

Andy stared at him. It was just as if he didn't know it had happened, hadn't seen it.

"Yes, you," the German said. "Why do I have to get lower in the water?"

Andy tried to swallow, but he couldn't. "You've got to—got to get lower—" Then he saw Owen's accusing eyes and he closed his own.

"Why?"

"So you can get under us. So we can lie in closer to you," Andy said. It was coming back now. He'd make it come back. They weren't sailing men. Little things. "Then—then, when we lie in closer, get a couple more cables to us and cant us over to port on your own underbody as you come up. That way the booms will lie to starboard across your deck."

"So? How do you know this?"

"I know how you're built. I read the magazines. And I know how our hull's built. That's all."

"You are a bright boy," the German said. "How is it you know what I intend to do? Is that in the magazines too?"

Owen turned his back angrily and spat overside.

For a moment longer the officer stared at Andy. His head and shoulders disappeared from above the steel bridge curtain, and they heard him call an order into the depths of his own boat. Nothing happened for a moment or so, then the *Sally* was no longer touching; she was free of contact, and the cables across her hung slack. At once the crew on deck took in scope and drew her closer. She ground against the sub again, and they took in more scope and they laid four more cables across her from the submarine, clewing them down and drawing them taut. The submarine lay much lower in the water now than it had at first. They'd changed trim and they were changing again. And then, very gently, the cables began to tighten of their own accord, biting deep into the *Sally*, crushing into her firmly, whispering with the tension as the sub rose a shade. And imperceptibly the schooner listed slightly to port, listed a little more, more, until she lay over at about twelve degrees. That way they could draw her main boom to starboard across the submarine abaft of the conning tower and screen, the tower with it from the eastward. Then they drew her fores'l boom over forward of the tower. Screening it to the west, and, with the topping lifts slacked off on the *Sally*, they secured the booms aboard the sub in that position. Bells rang, and the taut cables across the *Sally* rasped and cut, chafing her decks raw as the raider began to move.

The compass needle swung lazily around and steadied on a touch north of east. Owen looked at it mechanically, for something to do, looking overside to see what they were making. Four and a half to five knots. Testing to see what the cumbersome rig would hold at. Better not get much more than five, Owen's mind said, or it won't look like sailing, if anyone sees us. Keep your mind on anything rather than think of Black Oke.

Andy sat with his back turned to Owen, thinking what Owen was thinking, but only thinking it around the edges of the wet red hole that Black Oke's murder had left in his mind. Doesn't look like sailing, if any boat sees it. But as he thought it, exultantly, it was as if the wind heard him and wanted to help the Germans. It hauled around almost two points and freshened perceptibly, bellying into the *Sally*'s canvas.

Two of the boarding party laid onto Black Oke's stiffening arms and hauled him to the companion. Bumped him down into the cabin.

Still Owen wouldn't look at Andy. The boy was feeling it now, knowing it. Owen thought he might never be able to look at him again. He could see him out of the corner of his eye, sitting on the locker top, knowing now what he'd done to Black Oke by talking, and helping them. Suppose I never can look at him again? Suppose I never can?

Eight o'clock. Eight or nine hours to No Man's. Five in the afternoon. Could they get away with it that long?

There were a whale of a lot of Navy wagons usually around Newport, going back and forth. Coming out or going in between Block Island and No Man's. But why don't they come? If it was only swordfish time! But it wasn't. Owen was biting his thumb.

There must be some boat out here somewhere. There must be some plane that'll come out and spot us. From the air, they ought to see what we're hiding, even miles away. Maybe, except from right overhead, we'd just look like a schooner to an airplane. No, no! Owen threw his head up and his muscles stiffened in his back. For a moment he thought he had shouted, because as he thought it, the lookout on the main masthead did shout and point to the south and east.

She doesn't look like a schooner sailing; any sailor'd spot her miles away, and someone has. That's what the kid did, and I've been cursing his soul for a fool—and now it may be too late to tell him.

Not twenty feet from Owen they were swinging that murderous deck gun around, elevating her, laying her to fire across the *Sally*. The men on the schooner leaped wildly off her to the submarine. There were two more machine guns on the sub's bridge suddenly. Men were standing by the cables to slip them on order, and they were all straining their eyes to the south and east. Smoke boiling down close to the water. Black smoke. Full-speed, forced-draft smoke, and four hundred yards ahead, a beautiful thin spindle of water leaping straight up into the sunlight. They could see the destroyer's boiling bone now, white and high and furious.

Andy had sprung up from the locker top, standing there, unable to breathe. Someone had spotted what he'd made wrong about it all. And the destroyer had fired for them to heave ho. He watched the Germans crouching to fight.

Owen stepped closer to Andy and gripped his hand where it hung at his side. "Good, kid, good! They still don't know!"

Suddenly the sub's skipper shouted, and the men at the cables slipped them. The *Sally* lurched and threw out a flat sheet of water to port as they let her go. She whipped her sticks, and her canvas cracked overhead. Then the sub's engines roared, and diesel smoke fanned across the wallowing schooner. Water boiled all along her starboard side, and her booms clammed across her and whipped out to port as if they'd tear her sticks loose.

The sub fired her deck gun, and the blast of it tore the sound out of their ears, the air from their lungs, rocked them on their feet. There were four more spindles of white water thrusting straight up into the sunlight. And again four. Closer, pinching in on the raider. They could see the white-orange flame of her deck gun firing through the water spindles, swinging as the sub swung bow on to bring her forward torpedo tubes to bear, to narrow her silhouette.

The destroyer was huge now, careering down on them, and the firing of both ships shredded the morning, tore it to tatters, riddled it. Then a great gout of water leaped up over the midsection of the sub and whipped outward in all directions, with flame in it and black particles; whipped out and dropped back along the whole midsection length of the raider. But halfway back, it spurted upward again in another furious, torn sheet in the sunlight. And suddenly the conning tower was heeled over to port, and the bow with the net cutter was coming up out of water. Men were running forward along her narrow deck, their arms flung up. Leaping overboard headlong and head down. Then the water between the sub and the *Sally* was pocked in a thousand small splashes as if a great fistful of pebbles had struck into it. And pebbles were striking the *Sally*. But that didn't matter. What mattered was the awful grandeur of sea death—the sub rolling in and under so fast that it wasn't possible. Rolling like a great black log, with that destroyer still tearing down on her through the screaming wind. Passing clean over where the submarine had been, dropping two ash cans and circling beyond the rumbling mushrooms that came up from them.

Then she bore down on the *Sally* and spoke through a megaphone. "What's your story?"

"They took us over just before daylight. We've been with them ever since. They killed one of our crew. He's in the cabin. I'm Owen Jessup, the owner."

"You're lucky," the destroyer's captain said. "We've got some of the *Bannockburn* survivors aboard. One of 'em's a Nantucket sailing man. He spotted you through the glasses for a wrong-un before we did."

Owen shouted, "This kid got 'em to do it! They weren't sailors, none of them. They canted us to port and hauled our booms to starboard. The kid sold 'em the idea. He had us on both tacks at the same time, port and starboard. Any sailor'd spot that as far as he could see. He's Andrew Cassat."

"Wait a minute!" The destroyer's skipper turned to an officer behind him on the bridge. Then he called back to the *Sally*, "Tell him we've got his brother aboard, off the *Bannockburn*."

Mike sat in the dining room listening to Andy. "All right, all right." Mike raised his hand. "I've got it all now, and the answer is you don't enlist."

"Mike, I had to go before, but I've got to go double now. I can't ever get over Black Oke, unless I do go and pay 'em back more and more."

"You can't get over Black Oke completely, no matter what you do." Mike's voice was solemn. "Black Oke didn't lay down his life for you, but he died by mistake for what you were doing. What you were doing was right, Andy. You were selling them a little thing, a bill of goods that finally killed their ship and all but five of them. And that's big—just as I told you the little things generally are. But there is still Oke to account for—and dead Germans can't do it for you. You've got to account for him yourself, Andy. Because that officer couldn't shoot, you're alive and poor Oke's dead. So it's you who's got to be big now, to account for it. To pay Oke back for dying, while you lived. Black Oke is going up into our burial plot—with the whole story written out on his stone, so that you'll always remember why you're alive and never waste one chance you get in living. You're not enlisting."

"I've got to, I tell you. I can't go to college with this war!"

"You're not going on to college. Not the way you were. The newspapers in Boston are trying to make a hero out of you. We'll forget that, because being a hero is all right if the funny papers, but it ain't living. We won't forget, though, that the afternoon papers say that Senator Cassidy is appointing you to the Naval Academy, so you're not enlisting."

"Say that again."

Mike stood up and held out his hand for Andy's. "All right, admiral," he grinned. "That's the start of your life. Go to it full out. I'm going down to Owen's now; they're laying Oke out." He stood quite still for a moment, looking at his younger brother. A big, hard-bitten man, Mike, long years away from the scant tenderness of his own sketchy boyhood. And always a little embarrassed when he felt tenderness for this kid. He started to speak, and stopped himself. Then he said gruffly, "You're a good kid, Andy."

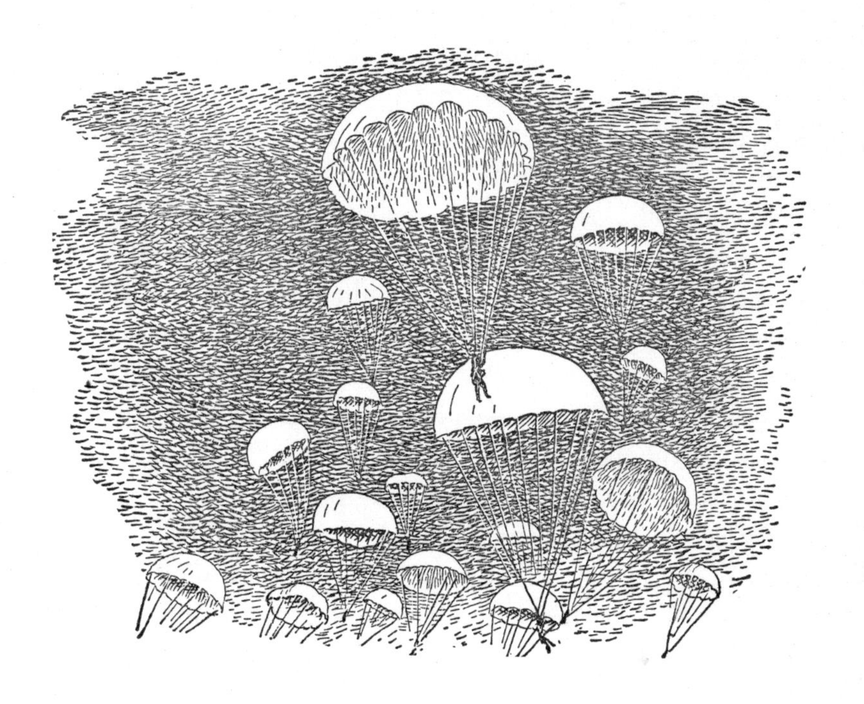

The Commandos Go In

BERNARD GLEMSER

The date was the twenty-seventh of February, 1942. The time was late evening. The place was the briefing room of an airfield in the south of England. The commandos stood around quietly, calm and relaxed. Nobody could have guessed that in a few hours they would be storming through enemy-occupied territory like fiends.

Paul, standing among them with Gaston at his side,

looked at them with admiration. In the past few days he had lived with them very closely; he knew them all by their first names, and they had accepted him as one of themselves. He had taken part in the many rehearsals for the raid; he had gone out on exercises, led by Major Cowles, who was to be in command of the raiding parties; he had eaten with these men, slept in a hut with them, and listened to their talk. They did not act or talk like supermen, he discovered. They seemed, in fact, to be extraordinarily mild and easygoing. But under that mildness was tremendous alertness; under that easygoing manner was great confidence in themselves and their comrades. They knew the strength of their combined striking power.

By now both Paul and Gaston had recovered from the effects of those eight nightmarish days of training. As the sergeant had warned, they were not commandos now; by comparison with the men in this room they were still rather like children. Even so, their bodies had hardened; they had learned that in an emergency they could call on hidden reserves of endurance. They felt alive and full of energy, as if they had just returned from a long vacation, instead of from one of the most rugged training camps in the world. They both felt that this night was going to be the greatest experience of their lives.

There was a rustle of interest as Major Cowles entered the room, followed by Professor Cheswick and Air Commodore Simpson. The major, a tall, broad-shouldered man, began to speak without any introduction. His voice was quiet, and he stood with one hand comfortably in his pocket.

"All of you know your jobs tonight," he began. "I'm only

going to run over the operation briefly in case there are any last-minute questions."

He faced the huge aerial photographs of Bruneval and the scale models of the farm, the house on the cliffs, and the Fire Bowl. Then he pointed to the Fire Bowl, which housed the radar installation.

"First, let me state again what it's all about. The Nazis have developed this device, known as radar, which is a definite menace to all our future plans. We could destroy it, but that wouldn't help us very much. We want to capture various parts of it intact, so that our scientific experts can examine it in detail. This is your primary objective. We also need to capture a few of the Nazi technicians who operate this radar, since they might give us some useful information; that's your secondary objective.

"Furthermore, this is an historic occasion. It's the first invasion, in force, of France since the Germans drove us back at Dunkirk in 1940. And we want to make it good. We are going to strike panic into the hearts of the Nazis and encourage our good allies the French. From now on the Nazis are going to realize that they are not safe anywhere.

"Now, as to details. You will fly in Whitley bombers and be dropped over the target area at midnight. The assembly point, which you will all try to reach immediately, is the ditch you see on the photograph here. Our young friend Paul Martin has described it to you very exactly. It's in the cover of a row of trees on the edge of the woods.

"You will be in three groups, each under its own leader. The first group will storm the house on the cliffs and deal with any Nazi troops found there. The second group is the technical group. These men will capture the radar post and dismantle it. The third group will clear the way to the beach, opening up the way for our return.

"When the beach path is open, all three groups will assemble on the beach and give the signal to be taken off. Landing craft will come in for this purpose. These will be covered by other landing craft that will guard your withdrawal. Covering these, in turn, will be motor gunboats and two destroyers, so that you will be well protected on the return journey. These naval forces, incidentally, are already on their way to Bruneval and have reported that they are making good progress. Are there any questions?"

There were none.

Air Commodore Simpson stepped forward, and said in his brisk manner, "I want to say a word about the flight arrangements. It's a perfect flying night—not much wind, a bright moon with a little cloud. Visibility should be good, and your pilots shouldn't have much difficulty finding the dropping area. You can expect some flak as you cross the French coast, but it will be light, I hope, and shouldn't give you any real trouble. We are also sending some planes to make a raid on a nearby area, which will draw off the enemy fighter planes located around Bruneval. I trust, therefore, that you'll have a comfortable trip."

Finally, Professor Cheswick stepped forward. He said with a chuckle, "I think this is the first time that science has had the help of a group of experts like yourselves. This is a piece of research that will go down in scientific textbooks as well as history books. That's all I have to say, and God bless every one of you."

"Thank you, Professor," Major Cowles said. He looked at his watch. "Zero hour for take-off is in fourteen and a half minutes. You'd better get ready, men."

The professor came hurrying toward Paul, and said, "How do you feel, my boy?"

Paul smiled at him cheerfully. "Fine, sir. I'm very happy that I shall be in France again soon, even if it's only for a short while."

"Take care of yourself," the professor said. "Remember, I have great plans for you when you come back." He turned to Gaston. "I'm relying on you to look after this lad, Sergeant. See that he doesn't get into any real trouble."

"Yes, sir," Gaston answered solemnly. "I'll keep an eye on him."

"Sir," Paul asked, "will the Resistance take any part in this raid tonight?"

"No," Professor Cheswick replied. "Not this time. We've warned them to stay in hiding, because there's too much danger of reprisals. But the day is fast coming when they'll take a full part in our raids. Don't worry about this now, Paul. Just be sure to come back safely."

The commandos were rubbing burnt cork on their faces and hands, leaving a thick black grime that would stay on for hours. They wore paratroopers' crash helmets, and they all carried heavy commando knives and hand grenades. Many of them had Sten guns—short, light Tommy guns that could pour out a terrifying hail of fire; some had automatic pistols. They were in very high spirits, laughing and joking as if they were going on an easy night exercise, not on a highly dangerous mission against the enemy.

They rocked with laughter as they saw Paul and Gaston cautiously applying the burnt cork, and they crowded around the two Frenchmen giving advice. At last Gaston said, grinning at Paul, "Eh, my little general! Even your own mother wouldn't recognize you now."

Paul grinned back. "And you, Sergeant, all you need is a banjo to make your fortune in a circus."

They were both armed with commando knives, but Paul had no gun. Gaston had both a Sten gun and a revolver.

The order came to assemble outside the briefing room, and the commandos trooped out and formed into squads in the darkness. Nearby, Paul could hear the sputter and whine of aircraft engines, bursting into shattering roars as they warmed up. As he stood at attention his hands were tightly clenched, and he could feel his heart beating rapidly. He was cold, but not with fear. It was like the line-up before a soccer game, when his body always tightened with expectation. He began to relax in a few moments, and he smiled to himself at the excitement of this adventure. He could never have imagined it in his wildest dreams; yet here he was, one of a company of commandos setting off for France. . . .

Then the darkness was split by a noise like the screeching of a thousand cats in agony. His blood froze; but at his side Gaston exclaimed, "Bagpipes!" Before Paul could get over his astonishment at the unearthly sound, his squad was marching toward the waiting planes.

The pipers led the way, stepping out at a steady pace, their pipes skirling Scottish songs that Paul had never heard before; but in some mysterious way the shrill sounds seemed to creep into his veins and make him tingle. It was the music of savage warriors, a noise that heartened men going into battle and terrified the enemy.

With the precision of guardsmen on a parade ground, the commandos marched around the perimeter of the airfield, and as each squad reached its plane it wheeled smartly. The pipes were still playing as the men entered the Whitleys. Paul found himself sitting on a narrow bench that ran along the side of the fuselage; with him was an almost unrecognizable Gaston and a horde of black-faced, grinning commandos. It seemed completely unreal. Then he heard the twin motors of the Whitley speed up, and felt the plane lurch as it began its slow waddle to the runway.

"Hold tight," Gaston said in his ear, and gripped his arm. The noise of the motors grew louder and louder, the plane seemed to be moving at incredible speed, and then all sensation ceased. He might have been sitting in an armchair in his own home. There was a cheer from the men, and Gaston's hold loosened.

An officer came over to Paul and looked down at him with a smile. "How are you feeling, laddie?"

"Fine, sir. Just fine."

"Try to get a little sleep. We shan't reach the French coast until shortly before midnight."

Some of the commandos were singing. Some were playing cards. Gaston brought two sleeping bags from a pile in the rear of the plane and handed one to Paul. "Curl up in this, my general. Make yourself comfortable."

"Thank you," Paul said. He lay curled up warmly, suspended in space, lulled by the steady purring of the motors, thinking of Bruneval, which he was about to visit in this strange way. How exciting everything is, he thought vaguely, and his mind wandered off into a pleasant fog.

The next thing he knew, Gaston was shaking him. "Put on your parachute," Gaston said. "We're nearly there."

Paul scrambled out of his sleeping bag, tightened his helmet, and fastened his parachute. Gaston checked it, pulling at the various straps to make certain they were secure, and Paul did the same for him.

"Twenty minutes more," Gaston said, "and we shall be flying over our own country."

All the men were standing now, lined up at action stations. There was no tension, no sense that they were going into danger. They were simply waiting to descend from the plane to do an important job. The Whitley lurched suddenly, and somebody said in a steady voice, "Hold on, boys. Flak." It lurched again and seemed to tip over slightly. The calm voice said again, "The Nazis have some flak ships down there. We're taking evasive action."

"Paul," Gaston said urgently, "stay close to me all the time. Remember. Stay close!"

A red light came on. The pilot of the Whitley was turning into the target. The hole in the floor of the fuselage through which the commandos would drop was open. The first men were already in position, waiting for the green light which was the signal to jump. Paul had practiced the routine many times already; he knew exactly what was going to happen, but he was surprised at the speed with which it was happening now, in actual combat conditions.

There it was! The green light! The first men had dropped . . . the line was moving forward . . . Gaston was behind him holding on to his shoulder, and for some reason Paul could hear the shrill wailing of the bagpipes in his ears again. Suddenly he himself was sitting over the drop hole looking down into darkness—an R.A.F. sergeant had hooked up his static line—there was a whispered *go* and he was through the hole and his legs were blowing sideways as he was caught in the Whitley's slip stream. There was a jerk at his shoulder as the static cord pulled his parachute open, and he saw it billow out and rise over his head, blotting out the sky. Then he was floating in a black silent world, without any sensation of falling, until the earth rose up slowly to meet him. He landed on it—in the midst of a soft white coldness—with a thump, and found himself being dragged forward. He grabbed the shrouds of the parachute, fumbled with the catch to release it, and tumbled on his chest into a foot of snow, gasping but uninjured.

Bruneval! But was this Bruneval? He stood up cautiously and looked around him. Yes. The woods were over to his left, the farmhouse and the house on the cliffs and the Fire Bowl were ahead of him, hidden in the darkness. He could see the gray shapes of the commandos against the snow, crouching as they ran to the assembly point in the ditch, and then he heard Gaston's voice calling quietly, "Paul! Paul!"

He called back, "Gaston."

"*A moi!*" Gaston exclaimed. "*A moi!*" The traditional French cry of comrades in battle: "To me! To me!"

Paul found him quickly, only a few yards away. "Are you all right?" Gaston asked anxiously, and Paul answered, "Yes."

"Let's get to the assembly point then. Hurry!"

They began to run. The snow blanketed all noise; the world seemed asleep. Even the throb of the Whitley bombers had dwindled. There was only this uncanny movement of silent men, all running swiftly toward the ditch under the trees. Scattered over the snow were cylindrical containers holding additional equipment for the raid—guns, dynamite, signaling apparatus. These the commandos scooped up as they ran.

"France!" Gaston laughed. "My beautiful France!" He snatched up a handful of snow in his stride, and held it until it melted, as if it were something infinitely precious. Paul knew how he felt. Even in these tense moments he was overjoyed at being back in his own land; every tree, every stone in his path was familiar. He had walked with his father and mother here, played at boys' games with his friends, and the recollection that the Nazis occupied it made him burn with anger.

"Here's the ditch," he panted to Gaston. For one awful moment he thought that it was empty, that some mistake had been made and the commandos had gone somewhere else. But then he saw the black-faced men crouching on their haunches, waiting motionless for the order that would send them into action, and he slipped quietly down among them.

"Here's Paul," somebody whispered, and he heard his name going down the line. "Paul . . . Paul . . . Paul." Then the whispering came back to him. The commando at his side touched his arm and muttered in his ear, "Squeeze past me, son. Report to Major Cowles."

This was no time for questions. He obeyed the order immediately, edging past the men until he reached the major.

"Paul Martin reporting, sir," he whispered.

"Paul!" the major said. "Thank God you're safe. Now listen. We go into action in three minutes. But all our men aren't here yet. I've just had a report that two of the Whitleys were driven off course by the flak and dropped their squads somewhere to the southwest, behind the woods. These were the men who had the job of clearing the way to the beach. They were expected to wipe out the machine-gun posts on the cliffs. Without them we may be cut off. Do you understand?"

"Yes, sir."

"It's possible that they're lost in the woods. This is what I want you to do, Paul. Stay here while we go forward. If these troops haven't arrived by the time you hear firing, go into the woods and find them. It's vitally important that they find their way to the cliffs. If those defenses aren't knocked out we'll never get down to the beach."

Paul's heart began to beat fast. He had known it all along. He had known that he could be of help to the commandos on this mission, and here was his chance.

"One minute to go," the major said, almost under his breath. He was staring at the sweep second hand of his illuminated watch. "Fifty-five . . . fifty . . . forty-five. . . ."

There was not a sound from the crouching commandos. Paul held his breath.

"Thirty . . . twenty-five . . . twenty. . . ."

Paul's hands were clenched behind his back. In his mind's eye he could see the machine guns bristling out of the emplacements that guarded the Fire Bowl, he could see the Nazis waiting in their dugouts, peering into the darkness for any sign of danger, never expecting that danger was so near.

"Ten seconds . . . five. . . ."

The major blew his whistle, a muted rattle like the choked, angry sound of a hawk about to pounce. That was all. Without any other order, the major crept out of the ditch and went running toward the house on the cliffs. Ranged on either side of him were the hunched, threatening figures of the commandos. And still there was no sound—no sound of clattering footsteps, no sound of clinking guns.

Then all the figures disappeared into the night. Paul, left alone, felt as if he had dreamed the attack had begun. The commandos seemed to have vanished utterly, like ghosts.

These first few minutes were critical. If the attack were discovered too soon the machine guns would open fire, mowing down and perhaps halting the commandos. But there was still only silence. Total silence.

The Nazis guarding Bruneval felt at peace with themselves. Most of them were in the farmhouse, sound asleep. Those others who were on duty were snug in their dugouts, and a little bored. There wasn't much to do, guarding this radar installation. After all, Germany was the undisputed master of Europe now, and there was nothing to fear from the Allies. True, a few bombers had flown overhead about ten minutes before, probably on their way to bomb some luckless town in Germany; but these bombing raids were ineffectual, and the Nazi night fighters would deal with the interlopers. Had not Adolph Hitler himself declared that

Europe was a fortress the enemy would never penetrate? Why didn't the stupid Allies realize they had lost the war? Why didn't they stop making foolish speeches about returning here? They sat in the machine-gun posts bored, half-asleep, waiting for their spell of duty to end so that they could go back to bed in the farmhouse and snore comfortably for a few hours.

The major had reached the house on the cliffs. Silently, his men surrounded it. The second group of commandos had reached the Fire Bowl. This, too, was surrounded without a sound.

An instant later came the signal for attack—a fierce blast on the major's whistle. Now there was no time to waste, no further need to move in silence. He dashed up to the door of the house, found it open, and rushed through. His men poured after him, guns and grenades ready to deal with any Nazi troops they found here. There were none in the rooms downstairs. The major went flying upstairs, shouting in a tremendous voice, "Surrender! Come out with your hands up!" A German soldier came out onto the landing, a rifle nervously in his hands, bewildered by this unexpected noise. Before he could fire, a bullet tore through his heart. He was the only occupant of the house, the major discovered. The Nazis had been so sure of themselves that they had not taken the trouble to put more than one man in it to guard it through the night.

Swiftly the major detailed a dozen commandos to hold the house. Since it stood between the farmhouse, where the main force of the Nazis slept, and the Fire Bowl, it could act as a barrier in case the Nazis attempted to fight. From the

Fire Bowl itself came the dull explosions of grenades, and the major went speeding through the snow to discover what was happening there. Six Nazis had made a hopeless effort to defend the installation; grenades had killed five of them and the sixth had been captured after making an attempt to escape. The squad of technicians was already dismantling the apparatus, while a number of commandos stood alert outside. Pieces of the precious equipment, so vital to the Nazis and the Allies alike, were being carried out swiftly.

But at the road that led to the beach only a handful of commandos lay concealed in the darkness, waiting to destroy the six or seven machine-gun posts that barred the way down. There were not enough men to take the post. They waited, hoping desperately that the remainder of their section would arrive so that they could launch their attack. Otherwise, those machine guns could hold up the entire raiding party long enough for the Nazi troops in the farmhouse to come into action. Suddenly they heard the first staccato clatter from the farmhouse—two machine guns firing erratically into the night, unsure who or where the attackers were, just firing blindly out of windows.

The way to the beach *had* to be cleared. Beyond the beach, a quarter of a mile out to sea, were the landing craft and the motor gunboats and the destroyers, watching anxiously for the signal to come in close to take the commandos off. Enemy destroyers and E-boats had passed them on patrol, and had miraculously missed them. But that, truly, was a miracle, and the small fleet was in deadly danger every moment it was stationary. If the commandos did not reach the beach soon, the Nazis would have sent out a general alert that would bring scores of their warships to this area.

That would bring, too, land reinforcements which would seal off the beach forever.

At the first sound of firing Paul slipped out of the ditch and went quickly toward the woods. His only weapon was his heavy knife, and he loosened it in its sheath so that it would be ready for immediate use if necessary. His mind was working very clearly. After he had gone a little way he stopped and stood with his head cocked forward, holding his breath. If the missing commandos had reached the woods he would hear some sound—the slight scrape of a boot against tall grass, the crackle of a branch underfoot.

He heard nothing. There was only the gentle sighing of the trees, laden down by snow.

He crept forward another hundred yards and listened again. Behind him he heard muffled shots; ahead, still nothing.

He reached the outskirts of the woods and began to work his way along them, toward the village where he had been born and had lived all his life. Then, in a low crouching rush, he went scurrying up a chalky bank, which gave him enough height to look over the nearby fields, and stood straining ears and eyes to catch some sign of the missing men. It was a dangerous place. A roving Nazi patrol might easily have spotted him here. But his personal danger no longer mattered; all that mattered was getting those commandos in action against the beach defenses.

He waited for several minutes. The cold air was beginning to numb his body. Suddenly he thought he heard a tiny sound over to his left, and he stiffened. The sound was not repeated.

Now he realized that he was in double danger. The sound

might have been made by a Nazi trailing after him, or by a commando tracking him down in the belief that he was a Nazi guard. He knew only too well how the commandos worked—creeping through the snow like cats, pouncing out of nowhere, killing with a single knife-thrust. They couldn't be expected to know that Major Cowles had sent him out to find them.

Was the sound made by a Nazi or a commando? There was only one way to find out. He took a whistle from his pocket and blew it very gently, his hands cupped over it, making a noise that might be a bird or a small night-prowling animal.

He waited for a reply. None came.

He blew the whistle again in the same way, repeating it in desperation. This time, clearly and decisively, a whistle answered. As soon as he heard it he went running down the bank, wildly calling out, "This way! This way!"

A voice snarled out of the darkness, "Who goes there?"

"Paul," he answered. "Paul," and stopped abruptly, realizing that the commandos would take no chances, that by now a dozen guns were leveled at him, ready to blast him into eternity if he made one false move.

A shadow wavered across the snow, followed by other shadows. "Paul *who?*" the voice demanded. It came from another direction now.

"Paul Martin."

"What are you doing here?"

"Major Cowles sent me to lead you to the machine guns overlooking the beach. We heard that you were lost."

The voice laughed. Paul recognized it as belonging to a Scottish sergeant. "Och, Paul, and thank the Lord it's you, laddie. But you took an awful risk standing in yon place. I nearly put a bullet through your handsome head."

"There's no time to lose, Sergeant," Paul cried. "They've begun to attack the Fire Bowl."

The shadows had reached him, had materialized as men in familiar uniform. "Aye, Paul, we heard the firing," the sergeant said. "We were making our way toward it, through yonder gap in the trees—"

"No," Paul interrupted. "I can show you a short cut through the woods. We go this way."

The sergeant blew a short blast on his whistle. "On the double!" he shouted. There was no need now for silence. The commandos were going through, no matter who tried to stop them.

"Lead on," he said grimly to Paul. "They'll be needing us. Let's get there fast."

The machine-gun fire from the farmhouse was growing fiercer. Bewildered by the unexpected attack, unable to guess how the raiders had reached Bruneval, the Nazis were making a confused effort to defend themselves. The major and his men calmly returned the fire, lying flat in the snow. They were grouped around the Fire Bowl, protecting it, trying to give the technicians every second they needed to complete their job. Equipment had already begun to move toward the cliffs. Everything was going as planned, except the final and most urgent task of clearing the way down to the beach. The major wondered whether Paul had been successful in finding the missing commandos, what was happening in the woods. . . .

In the distance, traveling along a road that led to the

farm, Paul saw the dimmed lights of three cars. They must be bringing up reinforcements, he realized, and there might be more Nazis following. It couldn't be helped. His first duty was to protect the men who were dismantling and carrying off the all-important apparatus. He and his commandos would stay to the bitter end, if it came to that, and fight a delaying battle to allow the apparatus to be taken aboard the landing craft. This was the purpose of the raid. It was his duty to see that it was fulfilled.

But the technicians had worked fast and efficiently. A corporal, wriggling flat on his stomach, reached the major and reported cheerfully, "The last load is on its way to the cliffs, sir."

"Have you set the demolition charges to destroy everything that's left?"

"Yes, sir. They'll go off in about three minutes."

"Good."

The major's whistle blew for retreat. Still facing the farmhouse, the commandos began to move back steadily, blazing away from a dozen different directions, confusing the Nazis, who must have felt by now that an entire Allied army had suddenly descended upon them. Their confusion was increased by the violent explosions under the Fire Bowl.

All that remained now was to get down to the beach and signal the waiting ships. But was the way clear? The major decided to find out for himself. He sprinted ahead, past the piles of equipment, and reached the gap between steep cliffs that led down to safety. It was dark here, and he could not see what the position was. The machine-gun posts, concealed in shadow, were silent.

Were their crews dead? Had the guns been knocked out?

He could not tell. His men were running toward him, and he blew a short warning blast on his whistle to halt them. Before anybody made another move, he had to find out for certain what had happened.

The commandos halted warily at his command. Then, from the beach, a gruff voice called, "Come on down. The boats are here. It's all right."

"Come on, men," the major cried. "Hurry!"

They began to move, but as they did so a voice called from the other side of the gap, "Major! Get back! The beach isn't taken yet! Get back!" At once machine guns opened fire. Two of the commandos fell.

"Flat on your faces!" the major bawled. "It's a trap!"

The machine guns had opened fire a second too early. The commandos snaked back, their bodies pressed to the ground, taking with them their two wounded comrades.

Coldly, the major considered the situation. After all this, after achieving full success in dismantling the Fire Bowl and bringing the equipment as far as the cliff top, they might be completely halted by the machine guns defending the beach path. It was bitter.

He shouted across the gap, "How many men do you have over there?"

"Major, only half my section. Not enough to attack all the emplacements."

The major bit his lip. He needed every man he had on this side to fight off the Nazis from the farmhouse and their reinforcements. And yet these machine guns had to be wiped out.

"Sergeant!" he snapped.

"He's been wounded, sir," a commando replied from the shadows.

"Corporal!"

"Sir!"

"Take nine men to reinforce the section across the gap. You will destroy the machine guns that fired on us."

"Yes, sir."

The major heard his men creep off and wondered what would happen now. You gave an order, destroy the guns, and you could trust your men to try to carry out that order. But it might not work out. Forty men could do it in a swift maneuver, attacking from different directions; twenty might be massacred. That would make the situation even more desperate. If only Paul had managed to bring the missing men here in time!

In a couple of minutes the action would start. He waited tensely.

The Germans in the farmhouse had not yet made any move. They still seemed to be dazed, uncertain what had hit them, and a group of commandos was still keeping them occupied with accurate fire, preventing them from showing their heads. But that could only last a little while longer. . . .

Then the major heard a shout, a wild sound that must have struck terror into the Nazis' hearts, *"Caber Feigh!"* "The Antlers of the Deer!" The war cry of the Scottish Highlanders. The shout came nearer, and he laughed aloud, knowing what it meant.

"Here are your men," he called vehemently across the gap. "Wait for them! Wait for them!"

In the growing clamor another voice rang out. It was Gaston. "Paul!" he cried. "*A moi! A moi!*"

The battle for the machine guns was short. A horde of ferocious commandos went swarming over the cliff, Tommy guns blazing, hurling their grenades into the sandbagged emplacements where the Nazis cowered under this paralyzing attack, wiping the crews out before they had a chance to fire. In a great savage rush, the black-faced men poured down to the beach, the Scots yelling their war cry, "*Caber Feigh! Caber Feigh!*" guns and grenades and the screams of the dying shattering the night.

Then, abruptly, it was over. A powerful voice called exultantly, "The way is clear, Major," and then quietly, efficiently, the secrets of the Fire Bowl were carried down, and the commandos took their places under the shelter of the cliffs. From the beach, bright with moonlight, a signal flashed out to the waiting ships to come immediately.

Gaston was hugging Paul with joy. "I thought you were lost in those woods forever, my little general," he said. "I kept wondering what I should tell the professor when I returned."

"This is my own country," Paul said. "I couldn't get lost in it."

The major came over, still tense and yet pleased. "You did a wonderful job, Paul," he said. "We shouldn't be here now if those missing troops hadn't arrived in time."

"Did we get all the apparatus from the Fire Bowl, sir?" Paul asked earnestly.

"Everything we need, my lad."

"What about casualties, sir?"

"We lost one man. Two were wounded. But I've just

made a quick check, and there are still seven missing. They belonged to the sections that were dropped away from the target area."

"Sir!" Paul cried. "Let me go back and find them."

The major said heavily, "No, Paul. I can't let you take another chance like that. You've already done your part."

There was a cry, "Sir! The boats are coming in!"

Grinding into the shallow water came the monstrous shapes of the landing craft, carrying fresh troops who could cover the commandos' withdrawal. A cheer went up as the ramps were lowered.

"Paul," the major ordered. "Get on board. Go with him, Sergeant."

Neither Paul nor Gaston dared to disobey the order. They waded into the icy water and clambered up the ramp of the nearest boat. Following them came three disheveled Nazi prisoners, and commandos carrying the secrets of the Fire Bowl. Too late, some guns opened up from the cliff top, but the guns mounted on the landing craft answered with a torrent of fire that silenced them.

There was no further opposition. A minute later the landing craft backed away and trundled out to sea, to the waiting warships. The raid was over. Triumphantly, the flotilla made for England.

In the warmth of a cabin, wrapped in blankets and still faithfully guarded by Gaston, Paul fell asleep.

He dreamed of Bruneval, which he was now leaving again for the second time. He dreamed of Bruneval, peaceful, quiet, free of the Nazis. In his dream he saw green grass and wild flowers growing where the Fire Bowl had been.

Not only Bruneval, but the whole of France was free; the people could laugh and talk as they pleased; the invader had been defeated and driven out. And in this dream somebody was talking to him.

It was the commando major saying, "You did your part," and Paul smiled in his sleep.

Leave It to Wilbur

ARCH WHITEHOUSE

In the 1942 issue of the *Salamander*, Brankley High School's yearbook, the scholastic history of Wilbur Doyle was duly chronicled, and he was bustled off to the wars. Beside a small studio photograph showing Wilbur with a stock graduation expression you may read:

Wilbur Hurst Doyle (Nickname—Wilb)
Course: Scientific
"A Goof of Plain, Uncoiled Constancy"

Wilb's main claim to fame is his ability to build boxes out of matches. He is reserved and shy, but has been heard to mutter items concerning model airplanes. He's a member of the Physics Club, sings in the *a capella* choir, and collects stamps. Wants to join the Air Service.

Class Prophecy: The darnedest things do happen.

No one wrote congratulatory jingles along the borders of Wilbur's copy of the *Salamander*. No football star deigned to scrawl his autograph across the team picture for him. He never even disturbed Mr. Blaithegate, his physics teacher, who would have been delighted to reward his star scholar with his standard algebraic motto festooned with his blunt-nib signature.

On the last day of school Wilbur took his yearbook home, tossed it on the bamboo-and-raffia table on the sun porch, and went upstairs to inspect his blue-serge suit, which he was to wear at the graduation exercises.

Later that evening his father picked up the *Salamander* and read Wilbur's scholastic record and the opinions as penned by the editors. He ruefully agreed that "A Goof of Plain, Uncoiled Constancy" was a fairly reasonable disposition of the evidence.

"Wasn't it nice that they mentioned Wilbur's stamp collection?" Mrs. Doyle said, as she knitted a few more rows before they started for the high school.

"Stamp collection—bah!" the former Captain Peter Doyle exploded. "Couldn't they have at least mentioned that he has been accepted for the Air Service? It just says that he *wants* to join the Air Service."

"You know Wilbur. He probably didn't tell anyone. He's

going to tell Arlueen Ridder tonight when he takes her to the graduation exercises."

"Well, that's one normal feature of the boy—at least he has a girl. But where the devil do these chits of girls get such names?"

"I think it's a pretty name." Myra Doyle pursed her lips with decision.

"You thought Wilbur was a pretty name, too," Peter Doyle observed. "Look what it got him! 'A Goof of Plain, Uncoiled Constancy!' "

"You don't even know what it means. Wilbur passed the Air Service examinations, didn't he? Butch Meakins and Sandy Tiller flunked miserably—and they were football heroes."

"I think he must have got the appointment on my record," his father ranted. "They do things like that in the Army. They probably thought he'd be like his old man—a heller on wings! I don't think he'll make a pilot; he never even made the Ping-pong team. No competitive spirit. I suppose he'll flunk out in primary and wind up inflating balloons for the meteorologist. I tell you, Myra, that boy simply doesn't have it."

"You don't know what he has," Mrs. Doyle said philosophically. "It takes all sorts to win a war."

"Do you mean to sit there and say you believe your Wilbur is capable of flying a four-hundred-mile-an-hour fighter plane, and shooting down those German bombers?"

"He's your Wilbur as much as he's mine!" Myra Doyle charged. "Looking back, I wonder how you managed to become an ace in the last war. You're an absolute menace with an automobile, and as for being able to read a map—do you remember the time we toured Cape Cod?"

"That's different! What you don't seem to realize, Myra, is that today I have to concentrate on other problems—the problems at hand. Being a research engineer demands long-view thinking. You have to think ahead; and I've done fairly well at it."

Peter Doyle had cause for his pride. The sun parlor was wide and well furnished. It looked out across a carpet of well-tended lawn. A blue-stone driveway curled through the grounds and splayed wide to the apron of a three-car garage. Peter Doyle had done well, once he got started; just as he had done at Verdun in 1918.

"I wouldn't worry about Wilbur," Myra Doyle said with quiet satisfaction. "I think I've taught him how to take care of himself and to recognize the value of things. That's the important thing in this world. You are able to accumulate things, Peter, but I'm the one who knows how to take care of them."

"But I've tried to talk to him and give him the benefit of my experience," Peter Doyle persisted. "He just doesn't react to any of it. I can't go and fight his war for him. I only wish I could. That's what's wrong with this war—not enough experienced men in it."

Peter Doyle felt better after that. He felt his words must sound good. The old *esprit de corps* and the courage to make sacrifices. He was almost certain he'd be willing to go in Wilbur's place.

"This is Wilbur's war," his mother stated. "We brought him into this world and gave him an education; we've taken care of his health, and you've provided him with a family tradition. I'd say that he was well-equipped."

"But he won't listen to me," brooded Mr. Doyle. "Still, as you say, he does have a tradition to uphold. That might help."

"I'm sure he has a sense of values, at any rate," Mrs. Doyle reassured him, as she put her knitting away.

Lieutenant Wilbur Doyle knew exactly what they were, the minute they pinioned out of the clouds. Months before he had known the exact identification details of the Focke-Wulf 190 fighter. He knew precisely what to look for and where to look for it.

The only trouble was in the values. He was up here alone and there were four Focke-Wulfs to consider. Four of them, all looking more like slim-flanked American fighters than like enemy planes. If you didn't look for the inverted gull wing, you might mistake them for Corsairs.

"We are going to do a simple offensive sweep," Captain Hardy had said that morning. "We'll break you in gently, Doyle. All you have to do is to stay in formation and watch what we do. Keep out of trouble, but if you start anything make sure you finish it—that I insist on. That's all."

Captain Hardy made it sound very simple, which was why he had become a flight leader. Hardy was one of those breath-taking gods with two sets of wings up. He'd been an illustrious member of the old Eagle Squadron serving with the R.A.F., when the war was just something noisy in the newsreels. The first Thunderbolt Squadron of the Eighth Air Force had been built around a number of Eagle Squadron men who had had much operational experience. That two-wing business had Wilbur stiff with respect. He had spent fourteen weary months collecting one pair; now he was expected to keep pace with men who sported wings on both sides of their uniform jackets.

On the day his name went up on the board for operational patrol Wilbur felt no sense of what he might interpret as fear. To fear, one must face something that one hates. Wilbur couldn't remember hating anything like that. It was the same thing as the sense of concern he struggled with whenever he had gone to class for an examination. His concern rested in the realization that what mistakes were to be made and charged against him were mistakes he himself was to make. The questions were there on paper, and all that was required of him was to answer them.

It was as simple as that—to Wilbur.

Taking off with the flight and crossing the Channel were simple, too, but when Captain Hardy snapped that wing-tip signal and started after three Dornier bombers, Wilbur tried to remember what the signal meant. By the time he had interpreted it the 'Bolts had somehow disappeared. He peeled off and tried to find them, but only got mixed up in the smoke coming up from Lille, which looked like black-shrouded ghosts devised to frighten him. Weaving in and out of these columns, Wilbur took time to ponder on his dilemma and then decided to go back upstairs and get a better look around.

That's when the Focke-Wulfs appeared.

Wilbur banked around to get a better view of their rudders—just to be sure. That gave him time to remember what his father had told him the night he left home to go to the troop-concentration point up the river from New York City.

"If you take my tip," Peter Doyle had stated with burly confidence, "you'll fight shy of those fighters. I mean, flying all alone just isn't for your type, son. I happen to know from personal experience."

Former Captain Doyle always made that point clear. It was another way of saying, "Don't forget, I was in the last war. I flew in the last war and I know what it's all about." Something that had happened many years before his own son was born was still a personal experience that somehow had become even more sharply defined by the kind rubbings of time. It was puzzling how he remembered every detail of his fight with three Fokker D-7's near Lunéville in September of 1918, when, as a matter of fact, he hadn't been able to make out a very convincing combat report an hour after he landed.

"I started out on DH-4's, where I had a gunner behind me," Captain Peter Doyle continued. "I liked having a gunner. In the first place it gave me a feeling of responsibility for someone and I always felt that there was someone there to take over, in case anything happened. You can get a 'creaser,' you know, Wilbur; and if your gunner can take over for only a few minutes, it gives you a chance to shake out of it."

What Captain Doyle was saying then was, of course, "I don't like seeing you go alone, Wilbur. I wish it could be arranged so that I could go with you. I'd even be willing to go again—as a gunner."

But Wilbur soon discovered he liked being alone. If he made a mistake he could compensate for it in his own way and no one would be the wiser. Wilbur had made a lot of mistakes, but he usually sat tight and thought it out, just as he had done at Brankley High when a knotty math problem came up. Of course, this mistake of losing Captain Hardy might take quite a lot of sitting out and a lot of concentrated thought.

A disturbing Focke-Wulf made a pass at him, but Wilbur pulled the stick back and climbed like fury.

"I mean to say," his father had explained, "two sets of eyes are better than one. If you miss an enemy formation, it's dollars to doughnuts your gunner will see them in time and tip you off. Then you can work up a system of teamwork, just as we did. My gunner would tap me on the shoulder to indicate which way he wanted me to turn. That's how we always got home. Take it from me, Wilbur, you'll be much better off in a two-seater where you have someone else to work with you."

Wilbur pondered on that and wondered where the German fighter had swished to. He drew his throttle back and tried to peer around. Something shot past him with a roar that made him huddle down in his seat.

"Next thing," his father had warned, "never let those Huns get on your tail. You're a gone cookie if you do. I mean, if you're flying single-seaters. Now, on the other hand, if you have a rear gunner, no Hun will attack you that way. They'll have to come in from in front and below—your blind spot, like."

Wilbur looked up and saw the blurred outline of a Focke-

Wulf's tail assembly rocketing skyward above him. Without bothering to snap on the reflector gunsight he pressed the button and eight guns spanked off streams of fifty-caliber stuff.

The Hun broke up as though it had flown through a large sieve. "I suppose I made a terrible mistake throttling back like that," Wilbur reflected. "I could have stalled badly and fallen off into a spin. I must watch out for that. I don't suppose anyone saw me, but if I'd been carrying a gunner—"

Wilbur wondered what he ought to do now. He wished he could find Captain Hardy and the rest of them. He wasn't sure where he was, and he didn't want to get lost completely and have to put a brand-new Thunderbolt down in enemy territory.

That reminded him of his mother, who had always insisted on his being careful with valuable things, like her punch bowl and the English mantel clock Uncle George had given her as a wedding present. Something about holding your breath when you wound it, to keep the dampness out.

The day Wilbur had come home with his commission bars and wings up she had asked about his uniform, and he had shown her the bill and explained that the Government had allowed him two hundred and fifty dollars for these expenses.

"But they seem too nice to wear while flying airplanes," Mrs. Doyle had said, fingering the material and inspecting the finish of the buttonholes.

"But we don't fly in these uniforms, Mother," he had explained. "We have special flying equipment: helmets and goggles and all that stuff. They issue that to you."

"Seems like a lot of money to spend on one boy," she fretted, as she adjusted her glasses. "And how much do those airplanes cost?"

Wilbur knew to the penny. He even knew how much a round of ammunition cost; he remembered seeing the figures on a war-bond advertisement. Wilbur picked up the strangest collection of information that way.

Mrs. Doyle sat down, stunned with the financial responsibility her Wilbur had assumed. "You must take care of these things, Wilbur. A lot of poor people are contributing from their small earnings every week to buy all this equipment. You must be careful not to break anything."

Wilbur had a confession to make. "I had one small crack-up at Westover when I was getting in some cross country on an AT-6. I guess I really wiped that undercarriage off."

"Oh, my dear! How much do you think that would cost?" Mrs. Doyle said that with the air of one about to remit payment immediately by check.

"Exactly two hundred and eighty dollars"—Wilbur produced the damage—"but I didn't have to pay for it, Mother."

"You must be careful, you know. We shall have to pay for it all eventually, you know."

This reminder came back to Wilbur the day he arrived at the Thaxted Air Station and saw the new Thunderbolts. The latest fighting equipment issued to the Eighth Air Force, they carried eight machine guns and did more than four hundred miles an hour.

Outside his cockpit the light was getting brittle, and Wilbur squinted about for a sign of the other Focke-Wulfs.

Something hit the side of his fuselage with a thud that sounded like beating the hull of a barge with a wet plank. Chunks of his Perspex hatch cover went flying in all directions.

The three Focke-Wulfs were coming in at him from a tight angle and Wilbur realized at once that they were really after him. So far they'd done considerable damage to his plane, and he knew there would be the devil to pay when he got back.

"You must remember," his mother had said, "you're an officer now, Wilbur, and you're responsible for everything they turn over to you."

There was an idea there, and Wilbur rammed the throttle up the gate again and pulled the stick back into his safety-belt buckle. The big Thunderbolt, retching and screaming through the pipe-organ vents drilled out of her fuselage, went up hard, curled over on her back, and Wilbur looked down and saw the Focke-Wulfs roar past.

"If you get in a jam," Captain Hardy had said, "stick her nose up, flop her over on her back, and let them go past. After that *you* should be in the driver's seat!"

There was something in what Captain Hardy had said. The German fighters shot away, hanging on to the tail of their leader, and tried to make out what this fool American was up to. Wilbur allowed the Thunderbolt to come around, completed the loop, blinked twice to kill the blackout, and charged in again.

The three F-W's huddled close for companionship, and Wilbur treadled his sight on the leader. He fumbled for the gun trip, pressed it, and the 'Bolt vibrated with speed pressure and the frantic recoil of the guns. The Focke-Wulf leader took the burst full in his tail assembly and ripped up into a mad, fluttering zoom.

That was just as well, for Wilbur, riding the air-speed indicator clean off the dial, went right through like a plummet and made the two wing men splay out. The leader hung at the top of his stall, twisted like a pike under the gaff, and started a flat spin on his back.

"They'll probably be able to fix some of those holes with a few dural patches," Wilbur muttered with a dash of wishful thinking as he came around again to get up into the sun. He wondered what he'd tell Captain Hardy to explain it all.

The two Focke-Wulf pilots were certain now that they were up against something particularly juicy. They agreed that their adversary was a crazy American—but all the Americans were crazy. Still, this one bore certain stripes of the exuberant youngster who doesn't know when to knock off. An Engishman would have his minute of joy unconfined, get in quick, make his kill, and buzz off again. That's how they stuck it through the Battle of Britain. Here they had a newcomer equipped with a brand-new *Dunderbolz* who was obviously intoxicated with his own program of success.

Already he had knocked off *Oberst-leutnant* Niglitsch and *Hauptmann* Waechter, for a certainty. That would make room for the advancement of a couple of mere *Oberleutnants*—especially if they could bring down this young bloody-taloned eagle. The two Focke-Wulfs drew off to consolidate their forces. There was at least an Iron Cross First Class connected to this somewhere.

Wilbur continued to circle, trying to make up his mind what to do and what to say when he got back. He dallied with the possibility of finding Captain Hardy and slipping back into formation on the assumption they would not have missed him. After all, the flight leader had been engaged with three two-engined Dorniers returning from a hit-and-run raid over the Thames estuary.

There was another headache. He would be expected to substantiate anything Captain Hardy might write in his report. Hardy might want someone to confirm any claim he might make concerning the bombers. That point brought up his own problem. He had shot down two Focke-Wulfs, but he would have a tough time trying to prove it. He didn't even know where all this was taking place and he hadn't noticed whether they carried any particular identification mark or number. When those Intelligence guys get at you, they can ask a lot of embarrassing questions, and if you want to rate as an ace you have to produce the evidence.

Arlueen had mentioned something about that before he left. It might be a good idea if he went over and got a closer look at them. They might carry squadron markings of some sort.

Wilbur swung over and pounded after them, encouraged by the memory of Arlueen, who alone had shown any interest in him at Brankley High. He liked Arlueen, because she was the only one who hadn't laughed when he explained about the Army Air Corps. He had told her about it in the garden while she picked flowers to make a corsage. Arlueen hadn't laughed; she just gasped, folded her warm brown hands over her breast, and stared.

"But, Wilbur," she said, really seeing him for the first time. "I didn't know!"

And Arlueen Ridder actually put her arms around him—and kissed him. Wilbur didn't kiss her in return. He just looked into her eyes and for the first time noticed how big and brown they were. They were actually saying the words her lips couldn't form. They were actually talking to him; they were saying, "But, Wilbur, this is wonderful—marvelous! I'm ever so proud."

"But I'm only going for training, Arlueen—with preflight training school first. I won't be a pilot for months."

But Arlueen would have none of it. She carried on and said the keenest things about him. Nice things, such as he was to be congratulated and that he must be very smart to get the appointment and pass the tests. She even said she would be very proud to have people know that she knew him—er—personally.

"Know me?" Wilbur quaked. "Why, you kissed me! That's more than just knowing me, isn't it? You don't kiss everyone who goes into the Air Corps—or do you?"

"Why, Wilbur!"

"But I just thought," Wilbur stammered, "that is, I thought," he began again. "I could write—that is, we could correspond while I'm away, couldn't we?"

"Oh, my dear," Arlueen faltered. "Of course. You must write to me. We'll write every day. That would mean something, wouldn't it? I mean—" Arlueen's eyelashes semaphored their triumph and affection.

"As if we were engaged, you mean?" went on Wilbur, blowing the last fuse.

"Of course—but just between ourselves, for now. It'll be such a lovely secret—until you get your wings. Then—then I'll wear your pin and everyone will know, won't they? Our very own secret given to the world on the silver wings of the Army Air Corps."

"Golly, Arlueen! You sure know how to talk nice," Wilbur gasped. "I *got* to get to be a pilot now!"

She led him away to a bench hidden by a trellis. Wilbur was really glad to sit down by now, regardless of the creases in his pants. Things were going blue, and bells were tinkling softly. Sweet smells he had never noticed before were wafted from the flower beds, and he wondered what a nightingale sounded like.

"Will you fly a bomber over Berlin, Wilbur?" Arlueen said, after a suitable pause. "You won't be afraid, will you?"

"Look, Arlueen," Wilbur replied. "No one knows whether he is brave or a coward. How *can* you know until you've been in danger? I won't know until I face it alone. That's why I want to fly a fighter—all by myself.

"You're always alone, in a fighter," Wilbur explained to her. "You're all alone, with just your thoughts. But I'd like that. It's clean and fair that way. You meet the enemy and you fight it out fair and square; and when it's all over and you've won, the victory is all yours. I guess it's because I've always been alone—with just my father and mother. In a bomber I'd be relying on someone else to some extent; on the gunners, the navigator, or even my copilot. This way, all the marks—both red and black—go down in your book. You can't borrow a piece of someone else's courage—you have to use what you have."

"Why, Wilbur!" Arlueen tried to stop her lower lip from trembling.

"And you get me right," Wilbur challenged, looking her full in the eyes. "I didn't read that somewhere and memorize it. I made it up myself. It's something I've been wanting to tell to my father, but somehow I guess I just feel sorry for him—being old now and trying to remember what he did in the last war; and I can't make him understand that it won't be necessary for him to go off again and fight *my* war."

Arlueen was overwhelmed. Wilbur Doyle had opened the doors on an entirely new world. Without realizing it they had passed out of saddle-shoed adolescence into the somber courtyard of maturity. Graduation and a valedictorian looking back could be no better than a costumed anticlimax.

"Wilbur," Arlueen said, moving closer, "I don't know just what to say, except— Will you kiss me, please?"

Wilbur did. That was that.

"We'd better be going now," he said, "but we understand each other, don't we? I mean, it's all arranged, isn't it?"

"It's your war, Wilbur."

A few seconds later Wilbur discovered the two remaining Focke-Wulfs were presenting him with more than his share of the war, special delivery. It was coming at him in high-speed jets from Jerry 7.92 guns, backed up by the air cannon tucked away in their wings. What they were doing to that Thunderbolt was more than Wilbur could stand. He already had enough to account for, without assuming the responsibility for any more. Captain Hardy would really be sore about this!

Still, if he wanted to find some mark of identification to

feed the Intelligence officer he'd have to get closer. The two Focke-Wulfs were converging on him now from a tight angle. Wilbur tried to remember what Captain Hardy had said about evading deflection shots, but his memory failed him completely.

The Thunderbolt took another scourging from the enemy guns. Wilbur gulped and kicked his rudder hard and wrenched the battered aircraft around to the right, creaking and protesting at the strain on her outraged frame. Without knowing why, he had broken up the attack, because he had sharpened the deflection angle and the Huns had to break off to avoid a wing-tip collision.

Wilbur continued his turn, banking hard, and lugged the stick back with all he had. On reversed controls the Thunderbolt whanged at the flustered Germans, who were still burdened with the problem of avoiding each other and evading this utter fool, who persisted in ignoring all the orthodox tactics of aerial warfare. It all added up to the fact that the inside Jerry found himself pinned between the flame-flecked gun barrels of Wilbur's 'Bolt and the dithering Focke-Wulf on his left.

Before he could make up his mind just what evasive action to take, Wilbur's guns had whipsawed his starboard wing away, and he fluttered into a flat spin.

Wilbur pulled up and came around again. He had caught the first part of the Focke-Wulf's factory marking, but he wanted to make a complete identification. That was Wilbur all over.

"The first part is DF," he muttered, jotting it down on a fixed pad near his knee. "I really ought to try and get the rest of it."

He went back after the tumbling F-W, which was now trying to wrap itself up into a ball. He could see the pilot struggling to get the hatch cover back and abandon the hulk. When the wing had broken away it slashed back and carved most of the tail assembly from the fuselage. It was well down by the nose now and trying to get rid of the other wing. There wasn't much left to work on, and Wilbur had to give it up and settle for the details of the dazzle-painted wings and the blue tips on the propeller blades.

As he watched, with professional interest, the efforts of the German pilot to get clear, he suddenly realized he had somehow managed to shoot down three of the four Focke-Wulfs that had attacked him. The impact of it left him wondering whether Captain Hardy would accept that to compensate for the damage. Three Focke-Wulfs ought to make up for the battering his own aircraft had taken. Of course, it would take a full crew, working all night, to repair her.

Wilbur wondered just how much the ground-crew personnel received an hour—and what they got for overtime. There were probably figures on it somewhere. He decided to look it up when he got back.

He tried to remember what Captain Hardy had told them about fighting Focke-Wulfs and what particular strategy to use. This might be a good chance to try some of it out. There was still another one about, somewhere.

"Now you guys needn't think that just because you're Americans and flying these new Thunderbolts, you're the pick of the pack," Captain Hardy had said only the day before. "Don't get the idea that one Yank is worth ten Jerries, because you're not. You're only worth about five," he had added with a mawkish grin.

"You're flying a great ship," he went on, "one of the best, but the other guys have some nice mounts, too. They learned a lot from the R.A.F chaps in the Battle of Britain, and they're coming back fast with the book open at the right page.

"Now you take this F-W 190 of theirs. You'll see a lot of them on the sweeps across the Channel. They're not the best fighters in the world, but they carry a load of bad news. The old Mess carried two rifle-caliber machine guns and a light air cannon. The 190 will greet you with two machine guns and four cannon. She can really dish it out.

"But don't worry about that. The Focke-Wulf can be taken. Don't try to get the pilot—he's carefully packed in Krupp plate. Her real weakness is the engine. They've loaded everything but the nutmeg grater under the cowling, and that's where we seem to get them every time. Pack a burst or two in there and you're sure to make her stink—that is, smoke up and quit. But once you start on these babies, don't give up. You finish the job—or they will. That's all."

Reflecting on this, Wilbur's orderly mind sorted the logic from the leadership hoopla and realized that Captain Hardy had missed an important point. "Still," he contemplated, "I should try out that engine theory. It wouldn't be fair to attempt to refute the captain's statement, without giving it a trial. Now where's that other Focke-Wulf?"

A few minutes later Captain Hardy, leading his eight-plane formation back to the Channel area after chasing a Dornier all the way to Namur, came upon a lone Thunderbolt engaging a Focke-Wulf. Hardy was a born leader, and he decided to stand by and use the exhibition for instructional purposes.

"Now I want you guys to watch this," he said over his command set. "We'll re-form into a packed V and sit above it—just in case he needs help. Now watch what happens."

They were first treated to the sight of the Thunderbolt ripping across the sky with a dash that almost swept the Jerry clean out of his coveralls.

"That was nice," commented the captain. "He has set himself a beautiful deflection shot. This ought to be easy."

But, instead, Wilbur leapfrogged and came around again. The German turned in tight and tried to zoom, but saw what was waiting for him up there. That gave Wilbur a chance to nose down and beat it back to a position dead on the Hun's tail.

"Now he has him cold," explained Captain Hardy. "This ought to be good. The kid's got a nice touch. Wish he had a movie camera in that kite."

But Wilbur had other ideas. Actually he was getting out of patience with the German, who somehow seemed bent on getting himself in the way—the wrong way! Wilbur swung off, came back, and once more was in a tight deflection-shot position.

"What is this, an act?" Hardy demanded. "Or is he playing cat-and-mouse with the poor guy? Maybe the kid's out of ammunition." Captain Hardy began to worry. "He's had several good chances already, but he hasn't fired a shot!"

"That's Wilbur," Pete Nyeland explained over his throat mike, "and you know Wilbur!"

The Jerry pilot was getting every swish of maneuver out of his aircraft now, and Wilbur was having to make the 'Bolt do more tricks than had been built into her. There was nothing else to do, if the captain's theory was to be tried out. The Hun was twisting and turning like a hooked trout, wondering why he was still in the air. Captain Hardy himself was not quite sure what was going on. "The kid really can fly—if that's Wilbur," he agreed, "but what's the idea?"

The two exhibitionists were packing home the knots now. The Focke-Wulf turned inside Wilbur with regularity, but Wilbur always recovered fast enough to set up another attack. Still, while he managed to get on the Jerry's tail or dead on for a broadside shot or even in a position to chance a deflection shot, he never released a round.

"This is getting monotonous," the captain grumbled. "The kid will fly himself clean off his base."

Suddenly the German saw an opening and peeled off while Wilbur was coming around after ignoring a chance from behind and below the Focke-Wulf's tail. Wilbur let out a low cry of dismay at realizing his enemy was running away. Still, he must attempt that "in-the-engine" attack somehow!

Hardy saw what was happening, but it was too late to stop it. The Jerry kite was in a scram dive. It would be fatal to go down after him. There was too much ack-ack around Lille.

"You threw your chance away, Wilbur," the flight commander argued silently, deciding to use all this as an object lesson later on.

But Wilbur wasn't through. There was still one trick left

in the Thunderbolt no Focke-Wulf could trump. Wilbur kicked over on one wing tip, peeled off, and went after him.

"No! Stay upstairs!" yelled Captain Hardy.

But the 'Bolt was on its way down for keeps. It caught the fleeing Focke-Wulf fifteen hundred feet below and passed it. Wilbur ignored the fact that he was reversing the original situation and giving the Hun a chance to follow on *his* tail. The heavy 'Bolt continued at bazooka speed while the perplexed Jerry wondered just what crazy Yank trick was to be played now.

Wilbur was clamped into his seat with the speed pressure, but he managed to screw his head around and check the position of the Focke-Wulf. Then, timing his trick to the second, Wilbur brought the stick back hard and reversed his direction completely. The Focke-Wulf was dead in his sights and coming at him at a million miles an hour. There wasn't any time for the delicacies of the game, so Wilbur pressed the gun releases blind.

The stuff went smack into the Focke-Wulf's blunt nose and proved Captain Hardy was right. There was a second when she flaunted a long back plume of smoke, which preceded an explosion that wiped off everything.

"—even the nutmeg grater," said Wilbur, ramming his stick forward to clear the mess.

"Just what was the idea, Doyle?" Captain Hardy demanded when they got back to Thaxted. "You had that guy cold about five times."

"But I'd tried all the other methods," explained Wilbur. "I just wanted to see how your theory worked."

"I don't get it."

"About making him stink—in the engine," Wilbur went on. "You see I had already shot two down by just clipping their tail assemblies, and another by shooting the wing off. I had to try your theory—in all fairness to you."

"Don't argue with him, Cappy," Pete Nyeland warned. "That guy says he got 'em, he *got* 'em!"

"Well, it was only fair to—"

"Wilbur," said the captain feelingly, "you're an ace, boy. You're an ace!"

"Oh, no, Captain," Wilbur protested, "I only got four. It takes five to be an ace!"

"You got five, Wilbur," Hardy insisted. "Four Huns—and me! I'm still in a flat spin."

I mean to say, you can't do anything with guys like Wilbur.

The Walls Are Breached

P. R. REID

At the beginning of the war, Allied airmen imprisoned by the Germans made many attempts at escape. The Germans were a little more lenient then. Later, when it became a game with the prisoners to try to escape, the Germans became harsher in their treatment. They sent these airmen to Colditz, a medieval fortress in the center of Germany thought to be escapeproof. It was floodlighted, patrolled by dogs, ringed by barbed wire, surrounded by walls and moats. They made one mistake, however; they brought together in one place the very best escape artists in the world. The prisoners pooled their talents. This story tells of the author's success in getting to Switzerland.

It was October 14th, 1942. As evening approached, the four of us, Hank, Billie, Ronnie, and I, made final preparations. I said, "Au revoir till tomorrow," to Van den Heuvel, and to Rupert, Harry, Peter Allan, Kenneth and Dick. Rupert was to be our kitchen-window stooge. We donned our civilian clothing, and covered this with army trousers and greatcoats. Civilian overcoats were made into neat bundles.

In parenthesis, I should explain why we had to wear the military clothes over everything. At any time a wandering Goon might appear as we waited our moment to enter the kitchen, and there might even be delays. Further, we had to think of informers—among the foreign orderlies, for example, who were always wandering about. If orderlies saw one of us leap through the kitchen window, it was just too bad—we might be after food—but it would be far worse if they saw a number of civilian-clothed officers in a staircase lobby—the orderlies' staircase as it happened—waiting, apparently, for their taxi to arrive!

Our suitcases were surrounded with blankets to muffle sound, and we carried enough sheets and blankets to make a fifty-foot descent, if necessary. Later we would wear balaclava helmets and gloves; no white skin was to be visible. Darkness and the shadows were to be our friends, we could not afford to offend them. Only our eyes and noses would be exposed. All light-colored garments were excluded. We carried thick socks to put over our shoes. This is the most silent method of movement I know, barring removal of one's shoes—which we were to do for the crossing of the sentry's path.

Squadron Leader MacColm was to accompany us into the kitchen in order to bend the window bar back into place and seal up the window after we had gone. He would have to conceal the military clothing we left behind in the kitchen and make his exit the next morning after the kitchen was unlocked. He could hide in one of the enormous caldrons as long as he did not oversleep and have himself served up with the soup next day.

Immediately after the evening *Appell* we were ready and started on the first leg of our long journey. It was 6:30 P.M.

I was used to the drill of the entry window by now. At the nodded signal from Rupert, I acted automatically; a run, a leap to the sill, one arm through the cracked pane of glass, up with the window lever, withdraw arm carefully, open window—without noise—jump through, and close again softly. I was through. Only two had done it before at any one session. The question was, Would five succeed? One after another they came. At least, they had not the window-lever latch to bother about.

The sentry was behaving himself. At regular intervals, as he turned his back, the signal was given. I could not see Rupert—but he was timing perfectly. I could see the sentry from behind the window throughout his beat.

Each time, as the sentry turned away, I heard a gentle scurry. I automatically opened the window, in jumped a body, and I closed the window again, breathing a heavy sigh. The drill was becoming automatic. It was taking as little as five seconds. Then, suddenly, just as the last of the five was due, I sensed—I do not know how—an uncertainty, a hesitation in the manner of the sentry as he turned away. I knew that he would behave oddly during this beat. My heart was in my mouth, for I expected to hear the scurry and anticipated a clash. But there was no scurry, and in the next instant the sentry stopped dead and turned around! It was nothing less than intuition on Rupert's part that saved us.

On the next turn of the sentry's beat, I heard the scurry, opened and closed again. At last all five of us were safe.

We removed our military clothing and handed it to MacColm.

I set about the window overlooking the German courtyard, and as darkness fell and the floodlights went on, I heaved on the bar until it was bent horizontal, and immediately attached to the unbent portion a long strip of black-painted cardboard resembling the bar. This hung downwards in the correct position and camouflaged the opening.

"All set!" I whispered to the others. "I'm going out now. Hank! Wait until I'm hidden by the shadow of the large ventilator out there. Then join me as quickly as you can. Billie and Ronnie, remember not to follow until we have crossed the sentry's path safely."

I squirmed through the hole in the bars onto the flat roof beyond. The roof joined the kitchen wall just below our window sill. I crept quietly forward in a blaze of light. The eyes of a hundred windows glared down upon me.

The impression was appalling. "Does nobody ever look out of a window at night?" I kept asking myself.

Happily there was shelter from the glare about halfway across the roof. The high square ventilator provided a deep shadow behind which I crawled. Hank soon followed. The sentry plied his beat not fifteen yards away.

For several days we had arranged music practices in the evenings in the senior officers' quarters (the theater block). The music was to be used for signaling, and we had to accustom the sentry in front of us to a certain amount of noise. While Major Anderson (Andy) played the oboe, Colonel George Young played the concertina, and Douglas Bader, keeping watch from a window, acted as conductor. Their room was on the third floor, overlooking the German courtyard. Bader could see our sentry for the whole length of his beat. He was to start the practice at 7:30 P.M., when the traffic in the courtyard had died down. From 8 P.M. onward he was to keep a rigid control on the players, so that they only stopped their music when the sentry was in a suitable position for us to cross his path. It was not imperative that they stop playing every time the sentry turned his back, but when they did stop playing that meant we could move. We arranged this signaling system because, once on the ground, we would have little concealment, and what little there was, provided by an angle in the wall of the outbuildings, prevented us from seeing the sentry.

At 8 P.M. Hank and I crawled once more into the limelight and over the remainder of the roof, dropping to the ground over a loose, noisy gutter, which gave me the jitters. In the dark angle of the wall, with our shoes around our necks and our suitcases under our arms, we waited for the music to stop. The players had been playing light jaunty airs—and then ran the gauntlet of our popular-songbooks. At 8 P.M. they changed to classical music; it gave them more excuse for stopping. Bader had seen us drop from the roof and would see us cross the sentry's path. The players were in the middle of Haydn's oboe concerto when they stopped.

I shall make this a trial run, I thought.

I advanced quickly five yards to the end of the wall concealing us, and regarded the sentry. He was fidgety and looked up at Bader's window twice during the five seconds' view I had of his back. Before me was the roadway, a cobbled seven yards wide. Beyond was the end of a shed and some friendly concealing shrubbery. As the sentry turned, the music started again. Our players had chosen a piece the Germans love. I only hoped the sentry would not be exasperated by their repeated interruptions. The next time they stopped we would go.

The music ceased abruptly and I ran—but it started again just as I reached the corner. I stopped dead and retired hurriedly. This happened twice. Then I heard German voices through the music. It was the duty officer on his rounds. He was questioning the sentry. He was suspicious. I heard gruff orders given.

Five minutes later I was caught napping—the music stopped while I was ruminating on the cause of the duty officer's interrogation and I was not on my toes. A late dash was worse than none. I stood still and waited. I waited a long time and the music did not begin again. A quarter of an hour passed and there was still no music. Obviously something had gone wrong upstairs. I decided, therefore, to wait an hour in order to let suspicions die down. We had the whole night before us.

All this time Hank was beside me—not a word passed his lips—not a murmur or comment to distract us from the job at hand.

In the angle of the wall where we hid, there was a door. We tried the handle and found it was open, so we entered in pitch-darkness and, passing through a second door, we took temporary refuge in a room which had a small window and contained, as far as we could see, only rubbish—waste-paper, empty bottles, and empty food tins. Outside, in the angle of the wall, any Goon with extra-sharp eyesight, passing along the roadway, would spot us. The sentry himself was also liable to extend his beat without warning and take a look around the corner of the wall where we had been hiding. In the rubbish room we were much safer.

We had been in there five minutes when, suddenly, there was a rustling of paper, a crash of falling tins, and a jangling of overturned bottles—a noise fit to waken the dead. We froze with horror. A cat leaped out from among the refuse and tore out of the room as if the devil were after it.

"That's finished everything," I exclaimed. "The Jerries will be here in a moment to investigate."

"The thing was after a mouse, I think," said Hank. "Let's make the best of things anyway. They may only flash a torch around casually, and we may get away with it if we try to look like a couple of sacks in the corner."

"Quick, then," I rejoined. "Grab those piles of newspapers and let's spread them out a little over our heads. It's our only hope."

We did so and waited, with our hearts thumping. Five minutes passed, and then ten, and still nobody came. We began to breathe again.

Soon our hour's vigil was over. It was 9:45 P.M., and I resolved to carry on. All was silent in the courtyard. I could now hear the sentry's footsteps clearly—approaching, and then receding. Choosing our moment, we advanced to the end of the wall as he turned on his beat. I peeped around the corner. He was ten yards off and marching away from us. The courtyard was empty. I tiptoed quickly across the roadway with Hank at my heels. Reaching the wall of the shed on the other side, we had just time to crouch behind the shrubbery before he turned. He had heard nothing. On his next receding beat we crept behind the shed, and hid in a small shrubbery, which bordered the main steps and veranda in front of the entrance to the *Kommandantur*.

The first leg of our escape was behind us. I dropped my suitcase and reconnoitered the next stage of our journey, which was to the pit. Watching the sentry, I crept quickly along the narrow grass verge at the edge of the path leading away from the main steps. On one side was the path and on the other side was a long flower bed; beyond that the balustrade of the *Kommandantur* veranda. I was in light shadow and had to crouch as I moved. Reaching the pit, about twenty-five yards away, before the sentry turned, I looked over the edge. There was a wooden trestle with steps. The pit was not deep. I dropped into it. A brick tunnel from the pit ran underneath the veranda and gave perfect concealment. That was enough. As I emerged again, I distinctly heard noises from the direction of the roofs over which we had climbed. Ronnie and Billie, who had witnessed our crossing of the roadway, were following. The sentry apparently heard nothing.

I began to creep back to the shrubbery where Hank was waiting. I was nearly halfway when, without warning, heavy footsteps sounded; a Goon was approaching quickly from the direction of the main Castle gateway and around the corner of the Castle building into sight. In a flash I was flat on my face on the grass verge, and lay rigid, just as he turned the corner and headed up the path straight toward me. He could not fail to see me. I waited for the end. He approached nearer and nearer with noisy footsteps crunching on the gravel. He was level with me. It was all over. I waited for his ejaculation at my discovery, for his warning shout to the sentry, for the familiar "*Hände hoch!*" and the feel of his pistol in my back between the shoulder blades.

The crunching footsteps continued past me and retreated. He mounted the steps and entered the *Kommandantur*.

After a moment's pause to recover, I crept the remainder of the distance to the shrubbery and, as I did so, Ronnie and Billie appeared from the other direction.

Before long we were all safe in the pit without further alarms, the second lap completed! We had time to relax for a moment.

I asked Billie, "How did you get on crossing the sentry's beat?"

"We saw you two cross over and it looked as easy as pie. That gave us confidence. We made one trial, and then crossed the second time. Something went wrong with the music, didn't it?"

"Yes, that's why we held up proceedings so long," I answered. "We had a lucky break when they stopped for the last time. I thought it was the signal to move, but I was too late off the mark, thank God! I'd probably have run into the sentry's arms!"

"What do you think happened?" asked Ronnie.

"I heard the duty officer asking questions," I explained. "I think they suspected the music practice was phony. They probably went upstairs and stopped it."

Changing the subject, I said, "I heard you coming over the roofs. I was sure the sentry could have heard."

"We made a noise at one point, I remember," said Ronnie, "but it wasn't anything to speak of. It's amazing what you can hear if your ears are expecting certain sounds. The sentry was probably thinking of his girl friend at that moment."

My next job was to try to open the door of a building through which one of our officers had already escaped. The door was fifteen yards away; it was in deep shadow, though the area between the door and the pit was only in semidarkness. Again watching the sentry, I crept carefully to the door, and then started work with a set of *passe-partout* keys I had brought with me. I had one unnerving interruption, when I heard a voice in the distance returning from the town. I had just sufficient time to creep back to the pit and hide, before the officer came around the corner.

It was 11 P.M. when the officer passed by. I worked for an hour on the door without success and finally gave up. We were checked, and would have to find another exit.

We felt our way along the tunnel leading from the pit under the veranda, and after eight yards came to a large cellar with a low arched ceiling supported on pillars. It had something to do with sewage, for Hank, at one point, stepped off solid ground and nearly fell into what might have been deep water. He must have disturbed a scum on top of the liquid, because a dreadful stench arose. When I was well away from the entrance, I struck a match. There was a solitary wheelbarrow for furniture, and at the far end of the cavernlike cellar, a chimney flue. I had previously noticed a faint glimmer of light from this direction. Examining the flue, I found it was an air vent, which led vertically upward from the ceiling of the cavern for about four feet, and then curved outward toward the fresh air. Hank pushed me up the flue. In plan it was about nine inches by three feet. I managed to wriggle myself high enough to see around the curve. The flue ended at the vertical face of a wall two feet away from me as a barred opening shaped like a letter-box slot. The opening was at the level of the ground outside, and was situated on the far side of the building—the moat side for which we were heading—but it was a practical impossibility to negotiate this flue. There were bars, and in any case only a Pygmy could have wriggled round the curve.

We held a conference.

"We seem to have struck a dead end," I started, "this place is a cul-de-sac, and I can't manage the door either. I'm terribly sorry, but there we are!"

"Can anyone think of another way out?" asked Ronnie.

"The main gateway, I think, is out of the question," I went on. "Since Neave's escape nearly a year ago, they lock the inner gate this side of the bridge over the moat. That means we can't reach the side gate leading down into the moat."

"Our only hope is through the *Kommandantur,*" suggested Billie. "We can try it either now, and hope to get through unseen—or else try it early in the morning when there's a little traffic about and some doors may be unlocked."

"Do you really think we'll ever pass scrutiny at that hour?" questioned Ronnie. "If we must take that route, I think it's better to try it at about 3 A.M. when the whole camp is dead asleep."

I was thinking how impossibly foolhardy was the idea of going through the *Kommandantur*. In desperation, I said, "I'm going to have another look at the flue."

This time I removed some of my top clothing and found I could slide more easily up the shaft. I examined the bars closely and found one was loose in its mortar socket. As I did so, I heard footsteps outside the opening and a Goon patrol approached. The Goon had an Alsatian with him. A heavy pair of boots tramped past me. I could have touched them with my hand. The dog pattered behind and did not see me. I imagine the smell issuing from the flue obliterated my scent.

I succeeded in loosening one end of the bar and bent it nearly double. Slipping down into the cellar again, I whispered to the others, "There's a vague chance we may be able to squeeze through the flue. Anyway, it's worth trying. We shall have to strip completely naked."

"Hank and Billie will never make it," said Ronnie. "It's impossible; they're too big. You and I might manage it with help at both ends—with someone pushing below and someone else pulling from above."

"I think I can make it," I rejoined, "if someone stands on the wheelbarrow and helps to push me through. Once I'm out, I can do the pulling. Hank had better come next. If he can make it, we all can."

Hank was over six feet tall and Billie nearly six feet. Ronnie and I were smaller, and Ronnie was very thin.

"Neither Hank nor I," intervened Billie, "will ever squeeze around the curve on our tummies. Our knees are not double-jointed and our legs will stick. We'll have to come out on our backs."

"Agreed," I said. "Then I go first, Hank next, then Billie and Ronnie last. Ronnie, you'll have no one to push you, but if two of us grab your arms and pull, we should manage it. Be careful undressing. Don't leave anything behind—we want to leave no traces. Hand your clothes to me in neat bundles, and your suitcases. I'll dispose of them temporarily outside."

After a tremendous struggle, I succeeded in squeezing through the chimney and sallied forth naked on to the path outside. Bending down into the flue again, I could just reach Hank's hand as he passed me up my clothes and my suitcase, and then his own. I hid the kit in some bushes near the path and put on enough dark clothing to make me inconspicuous. Hank was stripped and struggling in the hole with his back toward me. I managed to grab one arm and heaved, while he was pushed from below. Inch by inch he advanced and at the end of twenty minutes, with a last wrench, I pulled him clear. He was bruised all over and streaming with perspiration. During all that time we were at the mercy of any passer-by. What a spectacle it must have been—a naked man being squeezed through a hole in the wall like toothpaste out of a tube! To the imaginative-minded in the eerie darkness, it must have looked as if the massive walls of the Castle were slowly descending upon the man's body while his comrade was engaged in a desperate tug of war to save his life!

Hank retired to the bushes to recover and dress himself.

Next came Billie's clothes and suitcase, and then Billie himself. I extracted him in about fifteen minutes. Then Ronnie's kit arrived. I gave him a sheet on which to pull in order to begin his climb. After that, two of us set about him, and he was out in about ten minutes. We all collapsed in the bushes for a breather. It was about 3:30 A.M., and we had completed the third leg of our marathon.

"What do you think of our chances now?" I asked Billie.

"I'm beyond thinking of chances," was the reply, "but I know I shall never forget this night as long as I live."

"I hope you've got all your kit," I said, smiling at him in the darkness. "I should hate to have to push you back down the shaft to fetch it!"

"I'd give anything for a smoke," sighed Billie.

"I see no reason why you shouldn't smoke as we walk past the barracks if you feel like it. What cigarettes have you got?"

"Gold Flake, I think."

"Exactly! You'd better start chain-smoking, because you'll have to throw the rest away before you reach Leisnig. Had you thought of that?"

"But I've got fifty!"

"Too bad," I replied. "With luck you've got about three hours; that's seventeen cigarettes an hour. Can you do it?"

"I'll try," said Billie ruefully.

A German was snoring loudly in a room with the window open, a few yards away. The flue through which we had just climbed gave onto a narrow path running along the top of the moat immediately under the main Castle walls. The bushes we hid in were on the very edge of the moat. The moat wall was luckily stepped into three successive descents. The drops were about eighteen feet and the steps were about two yards wide, with odd shrubs and grass growing on them. A couple of sheets were made ready. After half an hour's rest, and fully clothed once more, we dropped down one by one. I went last and fell into the arms of those below me.

On the way down, Billie suddenly developed a tickle in his throat and started a cough which disturbed the dogs. They began barking in their kennels, which we saw for the first time, uncomfortably near the route we were to take. Billie in desperation ate a quantity of grass and earth, which seemed to stop the irritation in his throat. By the time we reached the bottom of the moat it was 4:30 A.M. The fourth leg was completed.

We tidied our clothes and adjusted the socks over our shoes. In a few moments we would have to pass underneath a lamp at the corner of the road leading to the German barracks. This was the road leading to the double gates in the outer wall around the Castle grounds. It was the road taken by Neave and by Van Doorninck.

The lamp was situated in full view of a sentry—luckily, some forty-five yards away—who would be able to contemplate our back silhouettes as we turned the corner and faded into the darkness beyond.

The dogs had ceased barking. Hank and I moved off first—over a small railing, onto a path, past the kennels, down some steps, around the corner under the light, and away into the darkness. We walked leisurely, side by side, as if we were inmates of the barracks returning after a night's carousal in the town.

Before passing the barracks I had one last duty to perform—to give those in the camp an idea as to what we had done, to indicate whether other escapers would be able to follow our route or not. I had half a dozen pieces of white cardboard cut into various shapes—a square, an oblong, a triangle, a circle, and so on. Dick Howe and I had arranged a code whereby each shape gave him some information. I threw certain of the cards down onto a small grass patch below the road, past which our exercise parade marched on their way to the park. With luck, if the parade was not cancelled for a week, Dick would see the cards. My message ran:

"Exit from pit. Moat easy. No traces left." Although I had pulled the bar of the flue exit back into place, we had, in truth, probably left minor traces. But as the alternative message was, "Exit obvious to Goons"—which would have been the case, for instance, if we left fifty feet of sheet rope dangling from a window—I preferred to encourage other escapers to have a shot at following us.

We continued another hundred yards past the barracks.

where the garrison was peacefully sleeping, and arrived at our last obstacle—the outer wall. It was only ten feet high here, with coils of barbed wire stretched along the top. I was on the wall heaving Hank up, when, with a sudden pounding of my heart, I noticed the glow of a cigarette in the distance. It was approaching. Then I realized it was Billie. They had caught us up. We had arranged a discreet gap between us, so that we did not look like a regiment passing under the corner lamp.

The barbed wire did not present a serious obstacle when tackled without hurry and with minute care. We were all eventually over the wall, but none too soon, because we had a long way to go in order to be safe before dawn. It was 5:15 in the morning, and the fifth leg of the marathon was over. The sixth and last stage—the long journey to Switzerland—lay ahead of us!

We shook hands all round and with "Au revoir—see you in Switzerland in a few days," Hank and I set off along the road. Two hundred yards behind us, the other two followed. Soon they branched off on their route and we took to the fields.

As we trudged along, Hank fumbled for a long time in his pockets, and then uttered practically the first words he had spoken during the whole night. He said, "I reckon, Pat, I must have left my pipe at the top of the moat."

Hank and I walked fast. We intended to lie up for a day. Therefore, in order to be at all safe we had to put the longest distance possible between ourselves and the camp. We judged the German search would be concentrated in the direction of a village about five miles away, for which Ronnie and Billie had headed and in which there was a railway station. The first train was shortly before morning *Appell.* Provided there was no alarm in the camp before then, and if the two of them could reach the station in time for the train (which now seemed probable), they would be in Leipzig before the real search started. This was the course Lulu Lawton had taken, but he had missed the train and had to hide up in a closely hunted area.

Hank and I chose a difficult route, calculated to put the hunters off the scent. We headed first south and then westward in a big sweep in the direction of the River Mulde, which ran due northward toward the Elbe. In order to reach a railway station we had to trek about twenty miles and cross the river into the bargain. It was not a "cushy" escape route, and we relied on the Germans thinking likewise.

We walked for about an hour and a half, and when it was almost daylight entered a wood and hid up in a thicket for the day. We must have been five miles away from the camp. Although we tried to sleep, our nerves were as taut as piano wires. I was on the alert the whole day.

"A wild animal must have magnificent nerves," I said to Hank at one point.

"Wild animals have nerves just like you and me. That's why they are not captured easily," was his comment.

Hank was not going to be easy to catch. His fiancée had been waiting for him since the night when he took off in his bomber in April 1940. It would plainly require more than a few tough Germans to recapture him. It gave me confidence to know he was beside me.

I mused for a long time over the queer twists that fate

gives to our lives. I had always assumed that Rupert and I would escape finally together. Yet it happened to be Hank's turn, and here we were. I had left old and tried friends behind me. Two years of constant companionship had cemented some of us together very closely. Rupert, Harry, Dick, Kenneth, and Peter. Would I ever see them again? Inside the camp the probability of early failure in the escape was so great that we brushed aside all serious thought of a long parting.

Here in the woods it was different. If I did my job properly from now on, it was probable that I would never see them again. We were not going back to Colditz; Hank was sure of that too. I was rather shaken by the thought, realizing fully for the first time what these men meant to me. We had been through much together. I prayed that we might all survive the war and meet again.

As dusk fell we set off across the fields. Sometimes when roads led in our direction we used them, but we had to be very careful. On one occasion we only just left the road in time as we saw a light ahead (unusual in the blackout) and heard voices. A car approaching was stopped. As we bypassed the light by way of the fields, we saw an army motorcyclist talking to a sentry. It was a control and they were after us. We passed within fifty yards of them!

It seemed a long way to the river. As the night wore on, I could hardly keep my eyes open. I stumbled and dozed as I walked, and finally gave up.

"Hank, I'll have to lie down for an hour and sleep. I've been sleepwalking as it is. I don't know where we're going."

"Okay. I'll stay on guard while you pass out on that bank

over there under the tree," said Hank, indicating a mound of grass looming ahead of us.

He woke me in an hour and we continued, eventually reaching the river. It was in a deep cutting, down which we climbed, and there was a road which ran along its bank. Toward our left, crossing the river and the cutting, was a high-level railway bridge. I decided to cross it. We had to re-climb the cutting. Sleep was overcoming me once more. The climb was steep and over huge rocks cut into steps like those of the pyramids. It was a nightmare climb in the pitch-darkness, as I repeatedly stumbled, fell down, and slept where I lay. Hank would tug at me, pull me over the next huge stone, and set me on my feet without a word, only to have to repeat the performance again in a few moments. Halfway up the embankment we stopped to rest. I slept, but Hank was on the *qui vive* and, peering through the darkness, noticed a movement on the railway bridge. It needed a cat's eye to notice anything at all. He shook me and said, "Pat, we're not going over that bridge; it's guarded."

"How do you know for certain?" I asked. "And how are we going to cross the river, then?"

"I don't mind if we have to swim it, but I'm not crossing that bridge."

I gave way, though it meant making a big half circle, crossing the railway line, and descending to the river again somewhere near a road bridge which we knew existed farther upstream.

Reaching the top of the railway-bridge embankment we crossed the lines, and as we did so we saw in the distance from the direction of the bridge the flash of a lighted match.

"Did you see that?" I whispered.

"Yes."

"There's a sentry on the bridge, sure enough. You were right, Hank. Thank God you insisted."

Gradually we edged down the hill again where the river cutting was less steep, and found that our bearings had not been too bad, for we saw the road bridge in the foreground. We inspected it carefully before crossing, listening for a long time for any sound of movement. It was unguarded. We crossed rapidly and took to the bushes on the far side, not a moment too soon; a motorcycle came roaring around the bend, its headlight blazing, and crossed the bridge in the direction from which we had come.

We tramped wearily across country on a compass bearing until dawn. Near the village of Penig, where our railway station was situated, we spruced ourselves up, attempted a shave, and polished our shoes. We entered the village—it was almost a small industrial town—and wended our way in the direction of the station. I was loath to ask our way at this time of the morning when few people were about. Instead, we wandered onward past some coal yards where a tramline started. The tracks ran alongside a large factory and then switched over to the other side of the road, passing under trees and beside a small river. We followed the lines, which eventually crossed a bridge, and entered the town proper. I was sure the tramlines would lead us to the station. The town was dingy, not at all like Colditz, which was of pleasing appearance. Upkeep had evidently gone to the dogs. Broken windowpanes were filled with newspaper, ironwork was rusty, and the front doors of the houses, which opened directly on the street, badly needed a coat of paint.

We arrived at the railway station. It was on the far edge of the town and looked older and out of keeping with the buildings around it. It had a staid respectable atmosphere and belonged to a period before industry had come to Penig. We entered and looked up the trains. Our route was Munich via Zwickau. I saw we had a three-hour wait and then another long wait at Zwickau before the night express for Munich. Leaving the station, we walked out into the country again and settled down for a meal and a rest behind a barn near the road. It is dangerous to wait in railway stations or public parks and advisable to keep moving under any circumstances when in a town.

We returned to the station toward midday. I bought two third-class tickets to Munich, and we caught the train comfortably. Our suitcases were a definite asset. My German accent was anything but perfect, but the brandishing of my suitcase on all occasions to emphasize whatever I happened to be saying worked like a soporific on the Germans.

In Zwickau, having another long wait, we boarded a tram. I tripped on the mounting step and nearly knocked the conductress over. I apologized loudly in German. "Excuse me, please! Excuse me, excuse me! I am a foreigner."

We sat down, and when the conductress came round I beamed at her, and asked in broken German, "*Gnädiges Fräulein!* If you please, where is the nearest cinema? We have a long time to wait for our train and would like to see a film and the news pictures. We are foreigners and do not know this town."

"The best cinema in Zwickau is five minutes from here. I shall tell you where to alight."

"How much is the fare, please, *Fräulein?*"

"Twenty pfennings each, if you please."

"*Danke schön,*" I said, proffering the money.

After five minutes the tram stopped at a main thoroughfare junction and the conductress beckoned to us. As we alighted, one of the passengers pointed out to us with a voluble and, to me, incoherent stream of German exactly where the cinema was. I could gather that he was proud to meet foreigners who were working for the victory of "Unser Reich!" He took off his moth-eaten hat as we parted and waved a courteous farewell.

Zwickau was just a greatly enlarged Penig as far as I could see. Dilapidation was visible everywhere. The inhabitants gave me an impression of impoverishment, and only the uniforms of officials, including the tram conductress and those of the armed forces, bore a semblance of any smartness at all.

Hank and I spent a comfortable two hours in the cinema, which was no different from any other I had seen. German officers and troops were dotted about in seats all around us and made up ninety per cent of the audience. I dozed for a long time and I noticed Hank's head drooping too. After two hours I whispered to him:

"It's time to go. What did you think of the film?"

"What I saw of it was a washout," Hank replied. "I must have slept though, because I missed parts of it. It was incoherent."

"This cinema seems to be nothing more than impromptu sleeping quarters. Look around you," and I nudged Hank.

The German Wehrmacht and Luftwaffe were dozing in all sorts of postures around us!

"Let's go," I said and, yawning repeatedly, we rose and left the auditorium.

Returning to the station in good time, we boarded the express to Munich. It was crowded, for which I was glad, and Hank and I spent the whole night standing in the corridor. Nobody paid any attention to us. We might as well have been in an express bound from London to the North. The lighting, however, was so bad that few passengers attempted to read. It was intensely stuffy owing to the overcrowding, the cold outside, and the blackout curtains on all windows. The hypnotic drumming and the swaying of the train pervaded all.

Our fellow travelers were a mixed bag; a few army and air force officers, some workmen, and a majority of down-at-the-heel-looking businessmen or government officials. There was not a personality among them; all were sheep ready to be slaughtered at the altar of Hitler. There was a police control in the early hours. I produced my much-soiled German leather wallet, which exposed my identity card, or *Ausweis,* behind a grimy scratched piece of celluloid. The police officer was curt. "Are you a foreigner?"

"*Ja wohl,*" I said. "To Munich and Rottweil."

"Why?"

"*Beton Arbeit,*" (that is, concrete work).

Hank was slow in producing his papers. I said, "We are together. He is *mein Kamerad.*" Hank proffered his papers as I added, taking the officer into my confidence, "He's a little stupid, but a good fellow."

The control passed on and we relaxed into a fitful doze as we roared through the night toward Munich—and Switzerland.

We arrived in Munich in the cold gray of the morning, several hours late. There had been bombing and train diversions.

I got in line at the booking office, telling Hank to stand by. When my turn came I asked for two third-class tickets for Rottweil.

The woman behind the grill asked for fifty-six marks.

"Karl," I shouted in Hank's direction, "I need ten more marks." Hank produced a ten-mark note, which I handed to the woman.

"Your identification," she said.

I produced it.

"*Gut,*" and she handed my wallet back to me.

I was so relieved that as I left the line, forgetting my part completely, I said in a loud voice, in English, "All right, Hank, I've got the tickets!"

I nearly froze in my tracks. As we hurried away I felt the baleful glare of a hundred eyes burning through my back. But we were soon lost in the crowd, and what a crowd! Everybody seemed to be traveling. The station appeared to be untouched by bombing and traffic was obviously running at high pressure. We had another long wait for the train which would take us to Rottweil via Ulm and Tüttlingen. I noted with relief that the wait in Ulm was only ten minutes. Hyde-Thompson and his Dutch colleague had been trapped in the Ulm station. The name carried foreboding and I prayed we would negotiate this junction safely. I also noticed with appreciation that there was a substantial wait at Tüttlingen for the train to Rottweil. It would give us an excuse for leaving the station.

In Munich I felt safe. The waiting rooms were full to overflowing and along with other passengers we were even shepherded by station police to an underground bombproof waiting room—signposted for the use of all persons having longer than half an hour to wait for a train.

Before descending to this waiting room, however, I asked for the restaurant, and roving along the counter I saw a large notice *Markfreiessen,* which meant coupon-free meals! I promptly asked for two, and also two liters of *Pilsner Bier.* They were duly served, and Hank and I sat down at a table by ourselves to the best meal provided us by the Germans in two and a half years. The *Markfreiessen* consisted of a very generous helping of thick stew—mostly vegetable and potatoes, but some good-tasting sausage meat was floating around as well. The beer seemed excellent to our parched gullets. We had not drunk anything since our repast on the outskirts of Penig, when we had finished the water we carried with us.

We went to the underground waiting room. We were controlled once in a cursory manner. I was blasé by now and smiled benignly at the burly representative of the *Abwehr Polizei*—security police—as he passed by, hardly glancing at the wallets we pushed under his nose.

In good time we boarded the train for Ulm. Arriving there at midday, we changed platforms without incident and quickly boarded our next train. This did not go direct to Rottweil, but necessitated changing at Tüttlingen. Rottweil was thirty miles, but Tüttlingen was only fifteen miles from the frontier! My intention was to walk out of the station at Tüttlingen with the excuse of waiting for the Rottweil train and never return.

This Hank and I duly did. As I walked off the station platform at Tüttlingen, through the barrier, we handed in our tickets. We had walked ten yards when I heard shouts behind us.

"*Kommen Sie hier!* Here, come back!"

I turned round, fearing the worst, and saw the ticket collector waving at us.

I returned to him and he said, "You gave up your tickets, but you're going to Rottweil. You must keep your tickets."

With almost visible relief I accepted the tickets once more. In my anxiety I had forgotten that we were ostensibly due to return to catch the Rottweil train and, of course, still needed our tickets.

From the station we promptly took the wrong road; there were no signposts. It was late afternoon and a Saturday. The October weather was fine. We walked for a long time along a road which refused to turn in the direction in which we thought it ought to turn! It was maddening. We passed a superbly camouflaged factory and sidings. There must have been an area of ten acres completely covered with a false flat room of what appeared to be rush matting. Even at the low elevation at which we found ourselves looking down upon it, the whole site looked like farm land. If the camouflage was actually rush matting, I do not know how they provided against fire risks.

We were gradually being driven into a valley heading

due south, whereas we wished to travel westward. Leaving the road as soon as possible without creating suspicion, we tried to make a short cut across country to another highway, which we knew headed west. As a short cut it misfired, taking us over hilly country, which prolonged our journey considerably. Evening was drawing in by the time we reached the correct road. We walked along this for several miles, and when it was dark, took to the woods to lie up for the night.

We passed a freezing, uncomfortable night on beds of leaves in the forest and were glad to warm ourselves with a sharp walk early the next morning, which was Sunday. I was thankful it was a Sunday, because it gave us a good excuse to be out walking in the country.

We now headed along roads leading southwest, until at 8 A.M. we retired again to the friendly shelter of the woods to eat our breakfast, consuming most of what was left of our German bread, sugar, and margarine.

We had almost finished our repast when we were disturbed by a farmer, who approached and eyed us curiously for a long time. He wore close-fitting breeches and gaiters like a typical English gamekeeper. I did not like his attitude at all. He came closer and demanded what we were doing.

I said, "We're eating. Can't you see that?"

"Why are you here?" he asked.

To which I answered, "We're going for a walk; it's Sunday, isn't it?"

At this he retired. I watched him carefully. As soon as he was out of the wood and about fifty yards away, I saw him turn along a hedge and change his gait into a trot.

This was enough for me. In less than a minute we were packed and trotting fast in the opposite direction, which happened to be southward! We did not touch the road again for some time, but kept to the woods and lanes. Gradually, however, the countryside became open and cultivated, and we were forced once more to the road. We passed a German soldier, who was smartly turned out in his Sunday best, with a friendly "Heil Hitler!" Church bells were ringing out from steeples, which rose head and shoulders above the roofs of several villages dotted here and there in the rolling country around us.

We walked through one of the villages as the people were coming out of church. I was terrified of the children, who ran out of the church shouting and laughing. They gamboled around us and eyed us curiously, although their elders took no notice of us at all. I was relieved, nonetheless, when we left the village behind us. Soon afterward, the country again became wooded and hilly, and we disappeared among the trees, heading now due south.

As the afternoon wore on I picked up our bearings more accurately, and we aimed at the exact location of the frontier crossing. A little too soon—I thought—we reached the frontier road, running east and west. I could not be sure, so we continued eastward along it to where it entered some woods. We passed a fork where a forest track, which I recognized, joined it. I knew then that we were indeed on the frontier road and that we had gone too far eastward. At that moment there were people following us, and we could not break off into the woods without looking suspicious. We walked on casually, and at the end of the wooded portion of the road we heard suddenly, "Halt! Who's there?" And then, more deliberately, "Where are you going?"

A sentry box stood back from the road in a clump of trees and from it stepped forth a frontier guard.

"We are going to Singen," I said. "We are foreigners."

"Your identification, please."

We produced our papers, including the special permit allowing us to travel near the frontier. We were close to him. His rifle was slung over his shoulder. The people who had been following us had turned down a lane toward a cottage. We were alone with the sentry.

I chatted on, gesticulating with my suitcase brazenly conspicuous. "We are Flemish workmen. This evening we take the train to Rottweil, where there is much construction work. We must be there in the morning. Today we can rest and we like your woods and countryside."

He eyed us for a moment; handed us back our papers and let us go. As we walked on I dreaded to hear another "Halt!" I imagined that if the sentry were not satisfied with us he would, for his own safety, move us off a few yards so that he could unsling his rifle. But no command was given and we continued our "Sunday afternoon stroll."

As we moved out of earshot, Hank said to me, "If he'd reached for his gun when he was close to us just then, I would have knocked him to Kingdom Come."

I would not have relished being knocked to Kingdom Come by Hank, and I often wonder if the sentry did not notice a look in Hank's eye and think that discretion was perhaps the better part of valor! A lonely sentry is not all-powerful against two enemies, even with his gun leveled. Our story may have had a vague ring of truth, but nonetheless, we were foreigners within half a mile of the Swiss frontier!

Soon we were able to leave the road, and we started to double back across the country to our frontier-crossing point. Just as we came to a railway line and climbed a small embankment, we nearly jumped out of our skins with fright as a figure darted from a bush in front of us and ran for his life into a thicket and disappeared. I could have assured him, if only he had stopped, that he gave us just as big a fright as we gave him!

By dusk we had found our exact location and waited in deep pine woods for darkness to descend. The frontier was scarcely a mile away. We ate a last meal nervously and without appetite. Our suitcases would not be required any more, so they were buried. When it was pitch-dark, we pulled on socks over our shoes, and set off. We had to negotiate the frontier crossing in inky blackness, entirely from memory of maps studied in Colditz. We crossed over more railway lines and then continued, skirting the edge of a wood. We encountered a minor road, which foxed me for a while because it should not have been there according to my memory, but we carried on. Hearing a motorcycle pass along a road in front of us, a road running close to and parallel with the frontier, warned us of the proximity of our take-off point. We entered the woods to our left and proceeded parallel with the road eastward for about a hundred yards and then approached it cautiously. Almost as we stumbled into it, I suddenly recognized the outline of a sentry box hidden among the trees straight in front of us!

We were within five yards of it when I recognized its angular roof. My hair stood on end. It was impossible to move without breaking twigs under our feet. They made noises like pistol shots and we could be heard easily. We retreated with as much care as we could, but even the crackle of a dried leaf caused me to perspire freely.

To compensate for this unnerving encounter, however, I now knew exactly where we were, for the sentry box was marked on our Colditz map and provided me with a check bearing. We moved off seventy yards and approached the road again. Peering across it, we could discern fields and low hedges. In the distance was our goal: a wooded hill looming blacker than the darkness around it, with the woods ending abruptly halfway down its eastern slopes, toward our left. There was no blackout in Switzerland, and beyond the hill was the faintest haze of light, indicating the existence of a Swiss village.

At 7:30 P.M. we moved off. Crouching low, and on the double, we crossed the road and headed for the woods. Without stopping for breath we ran, through hedges, across ditches, wading through mud, and then on again. Dreading barbed wire, which we could never have seen, we ran, panting with excitement as much as with breathlessness, across fields newly plowed, meadows, and marshland, till at last we rounded the corner of the woods. Here, for a moment, we halted for breath.

I felt that if I could not have a drink of water soon I would die. My throat was parched and swollen and my tongue was choking me. My heart was pounding like a sledge hammer. I was gasping for breath. I had lived for two and a half years, both awake and in sleep, with the vision of this race before me, and every nerve in my body was taut to breaking pitch.

We were not yet home. We had done about half a mile

and could see the lights of the Swiss village ahead. Great care was now necessary, for we could easily recross the frontier into Germany without knowing it, and stumble on a guard post. From the corner of the wood we had to continue in a sweeping curve, first toward our right, and then left again toward the village. Where we stood we were actually in Switzerland, but in a direct line between us and the Swiss village lay Germany.

Why had we run instead of creeping forward warily? The answer is that instinct dictated it and, I think in this case, instinct was right. Escapers' experience has borne out that the psychological reaction of a fleeing man to a shouted command, such as "Halt," varies. If a man is walking or creeping the reaction is to stop. If he is running the reaction is to run faster. It is in the split seconds of such instinctive decisions that success or failure may be determined.

We continued on our way at a rapid walk, over grass and boggy land, crouching low at every sound. It was important to avoid even Swiss frontier posts. We had heard curious rumors of escapers being returned to the Germans by unfriendly Swiss guards. However untrue, we were taking no risks.

We saw occasional shadowy forms and circled widely around them and at last, at 8:30 P.M., approached the village along a sandy path.

We were about a thousand yards inside the Swiss frontier. We had completed the four-hundred-mile journey from Colditz in less than four days.

Under the first lamppost of the village street, Hank and I shook hands in silence.

The Rifles of the Regiment

ERIC KNIGHT

Colonel Heathergall has become a bit of a regimental legend already. In the mess of the Loyal Rifles, they say, "Ah, but Old Glass Eye! I'll never forget once. . . ." Then off they go on some story or other about "Old Glass Eye."

But the regiment doesn't know the finest and truest story of all: when he fought all night with Fear—and won.

Colonel Heathergall met Fear in a little shack atop a cliff near the French village of Ste. Marguerite-en-Vaux. He had never met Fear before—not on the Somme or in India or in Palestine—because he was the type brought up not to know Fear. Fear is a cad—you just don't recognize the bounder.

The system has its points. Not being even on nodding acquaintance with Fear had allowed the colonel to keep the Loyal Rifle Regiment going in France long after all other British troops had gone—they were still fighting, working their way westward toward the Channel, nearly two weeks after Dunkirk was all over.

The men—those that were left—were drunk with fatigue. When they marched between fights, they slept. When they rested, they went into a sort of coma, and the sergeants had to slap them to waken them.

"They're nearly done," the adjutant said. "Shouldn't we jettison equipment?"

"All right," the colonel said, finally. "Equipment can be destroyed and left behind. But not rifles! The regiment's never failed to carry its rifles in—and carry 'em out. We'll take our rifles with us—every last single rifle."

The adjutant saluted.

"Er—and tell 'em we'll cut through soon," the colonel added. "Tell 'em I say we'll find a soft spot and cut through soon."

But the Loyal Rifles never did cut through. For there was then no British Army left in France to cut through to. But the regiment didn't know that. It marched west and north and attacked, and went west and north again. Each time it brought out its rifles and left its dead. First the sergeants were carrying two rifles, and then the men, and then the officers.

The Loyal Rifles went on until—they could go no farther. For they had reached the sea. It was on a headland looking out over the Channel, beside the fishing port of Ste. Marguerite-en-Vaux.

In the late afternoon the colonel used the regiment's last strength in an attempt to take Ste. Marguerite, for there might be boats there, fishing smacks, something that could carry them all back to England. He didn't find boats. He found the enemy with tanks and artillery, and the regiment withdrew. They left their dead, but they left no rifles.

The colonel sent out scouts. They brought him the report. They were cut off by the Germans—ringed about with their backs to the sea, on a cliff top with a two-hundred-foot drop to the beach below.

The regiment posted pickets, and dug foxholes, and fought until darkness came. Then they waited through the night for the last attack that was sure to come.

And it was that night, in his headquarters at the cliff top shack, that Colonel Heathergall, for the first time in his well-bred, British, military life, met Fear.

Fear had a leprous face. Its white robes were damp, and it smelled of stale sweat.

Colonel Heathergall, who had not heard the door close, saw the figure standing there in the darkness. "Who—who is it?"

Fear bowed and said, "You know me, really, Colonel. All your arrogant, aristocratic, British life you've snubbed me and pretended you didn't know me, but really you do, don't you? Let us be friends."

The colonel adjusted his monocle. "What do you want?" he asked.

"I've come to tell you," Fear said, "that it's time for you to surrender the regiment. You're finished."

"You're a slimy brute," the colonel said. "I won't surrender. There must be some way out! That R.A.F. plane this morning; I'm sure it saw us—the way the chap waggled his wings. He'd go get help. The Navy—they'll come!"

Fear laughed. "And if they come, then what? How would you get down that cliff? You *can't* get down—and you know it!"

"We could cut south and find a better spot—the men still have fight left," the colonel said desperately.

"The men," Fear said, "they'll leave their broken bodies wherever you choose. They've got the stuff. And oh, yes, you too, have courage, in your way. The huntin'-shootin'-fishin' sort of courage. The well-bred kind of courage. But that's got nothing to do with *this* kind of war. You haven't the right to ask your men to die to preserve that sort of record. Have you?"

The colonel sat still, not answering.

Fear spoke again. "The enemy will be here soon. Your men are exhausted. They can't do any more. Really, you'd be saving their lives if you surrender. No one would blame you. . . ."

The colonel shook his head. "No," he said. "We can't do that. You see—we never have done that. And we can't now. Perhaps we are outmoded. I and my kind may be out of date—incompetent—belonging to a bygone day. But. . . ." He looked around him as if for help. Then he went on desperately, "But—we've brought out all the rifles."

"Is that all?" mocked Fear.

"All?" the colonel echoed. "Is that all?"

Then at last he squared his shoulders. "All? Why, it's everything! I may die—and my men may die—but the regiment! It doesn't. The regiment goes on living. It's bigger than me—it's bigger than the men. It's bigger than you!"

And exactly as he said that, Fear fled. And there came a rap on the door, and the adjutant's voice sounded.

"Come in," the colonel said quietly.

"Are you alone, sir?" the adjutant asked.

"Yes," the colonel said. "Quite alone. What is it?"

"Report from the signal officer, sir. He has carried an ordinary torch with him, and he feels the colonel will be interested to know that he's in visual communication with the Navy—destroyers or something. They say they're ready to put off boats to take us off."

"Tell him my thanks to the C.O. of whatever naval force there is there. Message to company commanders: Withdraw pickets quietly. Rendezvous cliff top north of this H.Q. at three-fifty-five ack emma. Er—pretty good chaps in Navy—I've heard."

"Indeed, sir," the adjutant said.

So they assembled the men of the Loyal Rifle Regiment on the cliff top, where they could see out and below them the brief dots and dashes of light that winked. And there, too, in the night wind, they could feel the space and know the vast drop to the beach. Some of the men lay flat and listened for the sound of the sailors two hundred feet below them.

The officers waited, looking toward the colonel. It was the major who spoke, "But—but how on earth are we going to get down there, Colonel?"

Colonel Heathergall smiled privately within himself. "The rifles," he said softly. "The rifles, of course. I think we'll just about have enough."

And that's how the regiment escaped. They made a great chain of linked rifle slings, and went down it one at a time. The colonel came last, of course, as custom dictated.

Below, they picked up the rifles, whole and shattered, that they had thrown from the cliff top, and, wading out into the sea, carried them to the boats.

By this time the Germans were awake, and they let loose with everything they had. The sailors used fine naval language, but they got the men into the boats. The Navy got in and got them out.

That's the way the Loyal Rifle Regiment came home nearly two weeks after the last troops from Dunkirk had landed in England.

In the mess they still talk of the colonel. "Old Glass Eye," they say. "Ah, there was a colonel for you. Saved the outfit, he did. Knew the only way it'd ever get out would be down a cliff—so he made 'em carry all the rifles halfway across France. Knew he'd need the slings for that cliff. Foresight, eh? Great chap, Old Glass Eye. Never knew the meaning of Fear."

The Immortal Harpy

HOBERT DOUGLAS SKIDMORE

The runway spun beneath the *Harpy* and she pulled up from it like a thing that must leave the earth. She ate the air and blew it back across her body. The runway held its drab color up to her fuselage, then fell away, colorless and spent. The propellers ate on, sucking in the air, and she was free and air-borne.

They passed over the predawn dimness of the hangar and saw the fellows waving to them. Inside the *Harpy,* there was a slow, grinding noise as the landing gear retracted. Her pilot, Captain Jerry Lawler, let her ride, gaining height. The ridge dropped from sight beneath them, and nothing lay ahead but the Pacific and the clouds that came down and seemed to melt into it.

Jerry looked across at his copilot, Watts, and grinned, winking. It was an expression of mutual knowledge, a recognition of each other and what must be shared.

"I'll hold her up for a while," Watts suggested.

"Okay, I'll go back and beat the breeze," Jerry said.

"Good deal," Watts grinned, and a moment later he had the ship in his hands, alone for the first time.

"Atta girl, take it easy," he mumbled. Already he felt a trembling begin at his spine and move toward his shoulders. It moved down his arms, and he clenched his hands furiously, forcing the feeling to stop. Now, slicing through illimitable space, the feeling quieted in his arms, and for a moment the *Harpy,* like a proud horse, seemed to accept his mastery of her. She rode free and easy, racing down the sky. He had come to her with no family, but she, together with Jerry, and the rest of her brood, was his family now.

In his high, transparent plastic roost, Sergeant Walter Kazmierczak, gunner, saw light coming over the rim of the world. The same that had hours earlier covered his home, his girl, his place of life. He thought of the moving sun rays as being the light that had come down Walnut Street in Elmira, New York. It has gone around the world to find Ginnie, he thought, and I wish to heaven I was there with her. But he wasn't there. He was here on the *Harpy,* with those who served her. With Pon and Chief and Mike Sheren and the others wakened before the light by Jerry, who had called, "Get out of your sacks. I got something you guys'll be glad to hear. This is our big day. We hit them late this afternoon. Tomorrow morning, the marines and the infantry land."

The *Harpy* was pulling a little heavy, but she was hauling a terrific load. Her gas weighed on her, waiting to feed her, and the huge bombs in her racks made her stomach heavy. But she was on her way, and she seemed to know it. The *Harpy* wouldn't have it any other way, her radioman, Sergeant Mike Sheren, told himself, not any more than he would. The unstopping roar of the *Harpy*'s engines became a thing so familiar you didn't hear them, he decided. Then after your thoughts had been away from her, oh, thousands of miles distant, you laid off remembering other things and let your mind come back to her, and you were conscious of their roar again.

Mike had been on missions before. He had gone to Munda, and down to Rendova, and to Tarawa, and to scores of little atolls left burning and popping like magnesium dropped into the Pacific. After one such mission he remembered buying a half-dozen native handkerchiefs at a native store. He had printed *Mrs. Ida Sheren* in large, crooked letters, adding the street and town. Mom's going to be surprised, he thought, as he carried the package to the mail window. Afterward, he had looked at three P-40's running along the rim of the mountain, riding the air currents. That's where he wanted to be, he knew—up there in the sky, where things became clear and apparent. It was then that he felt that he stood at the beginning of a passageway which led to some kind of a world, somehow known, but unseen. He had noticed that there was a strong camaraderie among the infantry—a physical thing, something that came from hand-to-hand combat, from seeing men die on the ground beside you. It wasn't like that with him, Mike knew. The old *Harpy* carried her full crew, but it was only a handful of men; men who fought and lived inside the *Harpy's* warm fuselage. There was something that happened up here where he was, in the quiet, silent places where death waited, but he could not be sure what it was. He knew only the limitless ranges that fanned upward from the earth, and they had given him a curious feeling of expectancy.

Sometimes, on leave, when he felt that way, he said, "Let's get stinkin'," and Pon—Technical Sergeant Chester Poniatowski—would say, "You ain't just whistling, bud. Let's." But when the time came for the pouring of the musty, slightly bitter beer down their gullets, Pon would be on the ground in front of the *Harpy* or under her, looking up at her belly. They seemed to be standing guard over each other, Pon and the *Harpy;* even when they weren't on the ground any more, but were drumming above it, it seemed that way.

The *Harpy* was box-shaped and unappealing while she was inert, but once she felt the air against her wings, she seemed to change. She was graceful and proud, and flew with assurance, for she had been to battle before, and she went to it calmly again. There was something about the *Harpy* up here in the element she had been born to live in that made her more than a battling old bag of bolts. The *Harpy* had a spirit about her that could not be assailed even by death. Pon loved her and sensed the immense power that rested within her. He liked to go back and forth inside the ship, touching her and taking care of her.

Even with all the others locked with him in flight above the Pacific, he felt alone with her; the others shut out and away from his communion with the *Harpy*. He felt alone with her, the way he used to be alone with his car in a garage full of people. Below him, the water danced in the plane's movements. As the air hit the *Harpy*, the whitecaps rose and fell. This is the best life in the world, he told himself. There was no feeling like it. He wondered proudly what those doubters, who had always seemed amazed that he had been able to make the old jalopy run, would think now, if they could see the *Harpy* with the miles slipping by under her stomach, across her fuselage, and into the unposted spaces behind them.

Standing on her catwalk, he let his eyes take inventory of the way the neat wires ran down her inner walls, the thousands of mechanical parts of her, her guns, the slick bomb racks. He knew that it was silly, but often when he was alone with her he sensed that she was grateful to him. It was something he imagined, he knew, but he had worked with engines all his life, and he knew how they reacted—an engine was a thing you could depend on. If you were faithful to them, they would be faithful to you and would run forever. The *Harpy* hit a shallow bump and bobbed a little beneath him, and he thought, If we treat her right, she'll stay up here, clean and switchin' her tail at death after we're gone.

The hours went easily. All the crew checked the instruments of their particular functions, and looked occasionally at the restless blue surface beneath them. They felt a sense of freedom, being away from the earth and the things it held, and yet, more strongly than at any other time, they felt a part of a group.

By afternoon, Pon, like most of the others, had removed his shirt and trousers, and in his shorts he rode the *Harpy* down to the left of the dropping sun. Idly, he let his gaze rest on the coppery back of Sergeant "Chief" Washington, the *Harpy's* armament man. Only *coppery* wasn't quite the right description, Pon thought. Chief's skin, that rippled over long muscles, seemed to be made of thick cream and the cream diluted the dusty reddish hue. His cap was turned sideways on his black hair, and the long, square-brimmed visor stuck up above his right ear like a feather worn by one of his ancestors.

Then out of a tumbling mountain of cloud two P-40's came in, one at a time, and roared down the sky to meet the *Harpy,* like workmen gathering along the road. Those on the *Harpy* watched them, knowing they had a date together down over the horizon, and that it was going to be an important one.

Where they were, there were no markers for time or space, but they met as easily as if they had traveled this way a thousand times. His people had the same gift, Chief thought. A waste of land, hard shadowed under a molten sun, rolled into infinity with the heat wavering up from it, and strangers to it were lost and their bones were bleached white by that sun, because they could not read it and it was a place foreign to them. Yet to those who were at home in the vast, brown, crawling hills, there were innumerable signposts pointing the way.

The hours passed, with only the roar of the *Harpy's* engines to mark their going. Jerry Lawler, back at the controls, called to the *Harpy's* crew over the intercom, telling them to settle down. The ship was pulling easier, now that the greedy engines had drained some of her weight of gas from her. She moved steadily, not lagging or impatient, and the sureness and calmness of her journey spilled out from her and into his arms and hands, up through his body.

In the *Harpy's* tail, Norry—Sergeant Frank Norris—idly rolled the fifty-calibers back and forth, aiming indistinctly at the sky in mock battle. When he dreamed, he dreamed about being again at school, and about the graduation dance and the way Edith had looked in her first formal—the broad, pretty stripes that ran around the full skirt of her dress, the clean, suddenly mature look of her face. He had taken her home at midnight, and they had said good night very quietly and seriously. The things they had said to each other seemed to have new value then.

Not that he had much time for dreaming. The need for knowing the *Harpy* in all her moods, of doing a job for her, and doing it as naturally as breathing, possessed all of them. He looked at Lieutenant George Kristensen bent over the navigator's table. Krist kept his hair cut short, hardly an inch long, for he hated to have it falling over his face. No navigator in the Pacific could bring a ship down on a pinpoint atoll with the cool assurance that Krist had. When he said coolly, "You can take her down now," Norry and the others knew that it was as sure as driving down from the ramp of a towering bridge; the runway would be there. When he marked the spreading terror of a hurricane, his voice became emotional, and he sounded like the voice of the storm itself. Jerry called him "Old Elements," though he was only twenty-two.

The names of winds held poetry for Krist: monsoons, squalls and typhoons, tropical hurricanes, and all the storms of the temperate zones. They fascinated him just as the texture and the feel of each piece of his fifty-caliber fascinated Johnny Curtin. Johnny knew every inch of her. But though he had more than two hundred combat hours as a waist gunner, he was still uncertain as to what it was that caused him to be here on the heartless *Harpy*. Life had been on the sweet side: a good job, plenty of money and women, and if the boss got too cranky, he could tell him to go blow it. And then one afternoon the radio music had stopped, and into the quiet, sunny peacefulness a voice had come, clear and sharp. Hitler was marching his men through the shadow of the Eiffel Tower. I'll join up tomorrow, he told himself, and even yet he didn't know why.

The sun came in through the huge bubble of the nose turret and made a brave nimbus of Bombardier Lieutenant Frank Story's mustache. There was a shine to the day that reminded him of the mornings when he and Elsa hurried down Fifth Avenue in time to see the morning light come down through the stained-glass windows of the cathedral. He and Elsa always walked from the church exalted and proud of being alive. Looking down, he watched the backward-moving, foamy whitecaps, wondering if Elsa still went to the cathedral. He wanted to think that she did and that she was happy. It was the only vow they had made to each other. They had said, "Keep yourself happy. Keep yourself happy, now, of all times." He was happy, now, knowing their target, its installations, its fighter protection, just as the others of the *Harpy*'s family did. Only their happiness was serious and thoughtful, for they knew the enemy would give it up only when he no longer existed. But the target had to be blasted out. It stood as protection to one of the arteries to the heart of the enemy, and when men talked of it they were grave and their voices were quiet.

The *Harpy* was flying the Number One position. Behind her, two Liberators rode smoothly above the soft carpet of clouds. Mike watched them in their easy flight. Even in his heavy suit, his body felt light and free, and there was only the strong determination in his mind to remain alert. He passed his eyes around and around the unchartered spaces. He remembered the days he had gone on past the people shoving and hurrying along the streets, and for all of them he felt a quiet pity. There was no way of telling them how a man felt when his vision buried itself in the milky distance. He and the others knew a solitary communion here that made all the other things that filled a man's life trivial and transient. Often, riding through the great shafts of light that broke upward toward the sky, he felt as if he had glimpsed some part of another world, a place luminously beautiful. It had taken all fear out of him, and on a morning like this he felt that he knew what to expect when the inevitable arrived.

Beneath him, Krist bent over his charts. He knew that if a line had been drawn across the skies, he could show that they were not a yard off this course. He checked his charts again, but they had ridden these skies for so many endless hours and days that he knew the figures, the latitudes and longitudes, the stars and planets, as if they were markers on some insubstantial highway.

He snapped the intercom. "We should be there in thirty-two minutes," he said.

"Okay, Elements," Jerry answered. "Keep your eyes open, fellows. They'll be coming up soon."

Krist returned to his charts. It made little difference to him what happened outside the ship. That was not his job. He was to guide her there and guide her back. Almost irritably, he shoved his charts aside and placed a sheet of white paper before him. He thought he'd scribble a note, but he couldn't think of anyone to whom he wanted to write. It had been like this all his life, he knew. The things that made other people happy or miserable seemed always to leave him unmoved. As a child, he remembered, he had watched the other children playing, and wanted tearfully to join them, but he had no capacity for laughter and play. He often wondered if death would disturb him, but after deliberate consideration he could not tell himself that it would.

Down in the nose, Story decided it would be safe to finish a chapter before he laid his book aside. It was a frightening plot, and he read quickly, wanting to trap the murderer before the fighters came in on them. He checked the two thirty-calibers again, glanced at his bombsight, and then returned to the mystery novel.

Chief's brown eyes moved across the far distances,

glanced upward, and then looked down to the side. Nothing coming yet. There was a curious lightness about him, similar to fever, but he knew he wasn't ill. It was only the awful weariness, the fatigue that ached in bones and settled stiffly in muscles.

"Lower the turret, Walt," Jerry called over the intercom.

"Right. Going down," Walt answered. A moment later, he slipped into it and began checking his guns, his ammunition, his range mechanism, his gun sight, switches, buttons, and pedals. It worked as fluently as a ball twisting and turning in water. He remembered the day the mechanisms hadn't worked and the resentment that he had felt. In the days and nights that followed, he had learned that the war isn't an individual; it isn't one mechanism. It is the total of all men and their willingness to die for the things they believe. He had become a part of it now, he knew, and it was larger than any emotion he had known he could feel.

"Comin' in at five o'clock!" Norry shouted. "Four of them! Five o'clock! Three Zekes and a Rufe!"

The words, sharp and loud, ran through the intercom system, jarring the men as if their own nerves had been touched. It would be a long run. It was at least twenty minutes in to the target, and they would have the fighters on them all the way.

Walt swung his turret around and down, so he faced as if he were falling from some high precipice. As he started to turn, a Jap fighter and another and another broke through the clouds directly beneath them, climbing as if they had been fired from some gigantic gun. "Three at six o'clock! Comin' up at six o'clock!"

"Send them around here!" Chief shouted back, laughing.

The men tensed, waiting. The *Harpy* rode on her course, oblivious of the planes that attacked from below and to the rear, where they hoped to be protected by the upright rudders.

Walt held his fire, and then, as the spurts of fire began to break from the fighters' wings, he opened up. His guns rattled, and the tracers went to the left and ahead of the lead ship. Slowly, he moved back on it, but as his fire closed, the fighter flipped over on its wing and drove off to the left. "Comin' over at eight! Get her, Johnny!" he shouted, and pulled his fire back on the other ships.

They separated, one driving downward beneath the clouds, and the other making a wide turn to the right and pulling in just ahead of the fighters that drove in from the rear.

Norry let them have a burst. John swung his guns across and back, but they did not peel off.

It was then that the first bullet ripped up through the *Harpy*, tearing a small hole in the floor near Pon's foot. He heard the sound of the bullet rattling through the fuselage, and swore quietly. He wanted Jerry to roll slowly to the right, so he could get a shot at the plane which had sent the first bullet into the *Harpy*.

Now the two other belly-turret gunners opened up, and the planes rolled away, headed for the protection of the cloud bank.

"Comin' in at two!" Chief yelled. "Three of them! Two o'clock!"

He caught the closer one in his sight and held it there. He

waited, tense and ready, and then he let his fire go, raising it a little, pulling it down again, catching the fighter dead center. Suddenly, flames leaped up from it, but it did not falter or change its course. He gave it another burst, and now suddenly, flaming and smoking, it seemed to be on them.

"My God, there's a war goin' on out here!" Story shouted, and grabbed the gun beside him, giving the second plane a long burst. It peeled off to the left.

But it didn't seem to make any difference; it was too late now. The flaming ship did not seem more than fifty feet away.

In the cockpit, Jerry and Watts suddenly threw all their weight on the controls. They acted together, without speaking, and the giant *Harpy* flipped up her right wing as she turned her nose to the left.

Involuntarily, Walt flung his arms over his eyes as the ship passed beside him. He could see the pilot shoving hard to get himself free of the ship. He could see the straps of the parachute, even the dials that showed through the puffs of smoke.

The third fighter saw his chance and made for it. In turning to avoid the flaming ship, the *Harpy* exposed her belly. He turned on her and opened all his guns. Walt saw the tracers as if they were lines running from his eyes. He shoved his foot down, swung his guns and his turret. He couldn't miss now, for the thing was almost on top of him. It was running a seam of holes down the *Harpy*'s stomach. He gave the Zero everything he had, and held it on the plane until suddenly it seemed to explode in the air. What had been a plane was wreckage and bundles of flame falling down through the skies toward the ocean below.

Pon did not know he had been hurt until the *Harpy* righted herself, and he threw his weight back on his right foot. It crumpled beneath him, and then he felt the warm fluid draining into his soft leather boot. There was only the warmness, though, and no pain, so he raised his eyes and looked along the bottom of the *Harpy*. A series of holes, evenly spaced and whistling with the air that tore through them, ran up toward the bomb-bay doors.

Thank God, he thought, they missed the auxiliary gas tanks.

"Take her down," Krist said quietly. "Target three minutes ahead. Take her down."

"Get ready for anything!" Jerry called. He waited a moment to see if the *Harpy* responded. Her giant nose slowly lowered, and she rode down easily and surely. "They're going to throw all they've got at us!"

Only Norry did not hear him. He had ripped the phones from his ears and was trying to force his hands inside his flying suit. Something had ricocheted against the side of the *Harpy*. It had come down through his left shoulder, and now his fingers found the fragment. It was lying inside his shirt, halfway between his shoulder bone and his heart. He pulled it out and looked at it, though his fingers were already freezing from the cold air. He let the shrapnel rest in his hands, holding his body backward from the handles of his guns, and he smiled slightly. The rest he had wanted was coming now. It was slipping up his legs and arms and gathering in his stomach. He thought that the next time he wrote home he'd tell Mom and Dad how the rest had come, and then he decided to let his head fall forward, so he could sleep easier. But as he moved, the *Harpy* dropped her nose downward, her giant tail pointed upward in the sky, and he looked into the clear whiteness above. It seemed that he could touch it, if only he didn't want to rest so badly. It seemed that he could reach out and touch everything that was in the heavens, only he wanted to rest.

As the *Harpy* came down through the clouds, the target lay ahead and to the north. Story looked quickly along the palms which fringed the beach, remembering the photographs he had studied so often. That was the ammunition dump ahead, where the low sheds huddled beneath the palms. That was where he was going to lay them. There was an immense dark cloud above the enemy base. It would make fine cover to head into as soon as they dumped the eggs. He moved his eyes back and across, wondering what had happened to the formation which had gone in ahead of them. And then he saw what it was. The dark cloud was ack-ack smoke. It was so heavy it looked as if you could walk on it. "They're sure sending it up," he said softly. The whispered words ran back through the intercom, back through the *Harpy*, and ended in Norry's insensible ears.

Watts reached over and grabbed Jerry by the arm, pointing down and to the right with his free hand. They were doing better than a hundred and fifty, and Jerry leaned forward, looking out toward the sea. The lagoon seemed to rush toward him. But his eyes caught and held. The enemy was moving in innumerable reinforcements for the attack. They were unloading men and equipment.

"Look at those ducks!" he yelled. "Look at them!"

In the belly turret, Walt swung his gun around to five o'clock. He had to see the ships. They were unloading crack troops, men trained to fight on the atolls, indoctrinated with a love of death. They would be waiting tomorrow to attack the American marines and infantrymen as they piled out of the landing barges and raced across the reef and up the beach. He knew what would happen to the men as the doors of the LCI's dropped down. The men would have to hit the water running. They would hit shoulder-deep, trying to hold their rifles above their heads. The treacherous, uneven coral would make progress slow and unsteady, holding the men like slowly trudging targets.

In those awful moments, the hundreds of enemy soldiers, fresh and fanatic, would open up on them. Unable to move back, with a rain of fire rippling the water before them, the men would be trapped. They would die there, fixed by the water.

"Let's get them, Jerry!" Story shouted. "Let me pick them off!"

For a moment, Jerry hesitated. All his training, his knowledge, the long months of his flying, told him that he had to stick to the planned attack. The objectives must be hit. That was the only way it worked.

"Stick to your targets!' he ordered.

"They'll wipe them out tomorrow, Jerry! There are thousands of them!"

Jerry looked down and he knew he could not keep the realization away for long. The water below him held victory or failure. All the weeks of raids, of planning and training, would be lost. The stroke that would break the enemy's lines in the South Pacific would be turned back, snapped and buried in the blue water. Even the *Harpy* seemed to see her destined glory, but he righted in his seat and pulled her back on her course.

"Comin' in at one o'clock!" Mike yelled.

Suddenly the intercom was shrieking wildly. Chief and Mike and Johnny all saw them. Three of them were coming down as if they were rushing at the peaked end of lightning. Mike held his fire until they closed to eight hundred and then he gave them a long burst.

There was nothing to do but wait, John knew. If they peeled off on his side, he would get a crack at them. It was less than the shaving of a second, but he waited impatiently. His eye was ringed by the familiar sight, the stubby grips in his hands, his thumbs extended and ready. This was the one moment in which he felt no urge to be elsewhere. He felt as if suddenly a picture of himself had been brought into focus.

The Zekes screamed, pulling up. Mike gave them another burst. It was so close he could see the slugs hit the cowling as if he were throwing stones against it. "Comin' over, Pon!" he yelled.

Pon hobbled a little to the rear of his slot, swung his gun, and as the smoking ship pulled up beyond the *Harpy,* stalling in her climb, he let his fire go. The Zeke seemed to hang there for a moment, as if the bullets had pinned it to the sky. Then it slid down and spilled over into a flaming descent.

Mike never saw the two others. Abruptly, the *Harpy*

leaped sideways, fell downward. It seemed to have been struck by a tremendous hammer. He heard the shattering rip of metal, the rain-spattering sound of the small shrapnel, and as he hit the floor by the radio cabinet, the *Harpy* caught heavily in the air. He could feel the jarring halt. As he straightened, Krist tumbled onto the same spot where he had fallen. He just lay there clutching his chest with one hand and ripping the oxygen mask from his face with the other. Mike straightened him out, shoved the mask back on his face, and jumped up to his gun again.

Krist could feel the oxygen running along his nose and down into his lungs. It was a pleasant and cooling sensation, but he dismissed it as temporary. He wished he had his glasses on. Perhaps he could see better, he thought, but he dismissed that too. It wasn't important. It was the terrible storm going on outside that was important. He wanted to get to his feet, grab up his charts, and see where he had made his mistake. Somewhere he had miscalculated, he told himself.

He brought his hands up, placing them on the floor at either side of his head, thinking he could push himself to his feet. He felt a deep revulsion growing in his stunned entrails. It swept upward, as if he would disgorge everything inside himself, but the nauseous wave passed into his head, clarifying it, and in that moment he felt a great release. Recognition grew slowly in his mind, and it left his tattered body trembling. I hate them, he said silently. I hate them. I have always hated them. I have hated them as long as I can remember, and it has made me fight. There had been this hatred in him, and it had kept him bent incessantly over his charts. The *Harpy* had never once been off her course. He had taken her to the enemy and brought her back, and he had never failed.

The *Harpy* was still rocking violently. It seemed to Mike that it took him forever to get his intercom working again. And all the time he was working with it, he kept repeating, No, not yet, not yet.

Story bent slowly over his bombsight. The ack-ack was coming up so thick that the trees and shacks were becoming indistinct. I'll put it right in their lap, he thought. He began yelling for Jerry to pull her over.

Walt pulled his turret up. The stuff was spraying around him like hail hurled upward. He wanted to get his face up. This might be it. It has to come sometime, and this might be it, he kept telling himself, but I don't want to get it in the face. I don't want it in the face.

Pon swung his waist gun around. The fighters were gone. They were taking cover down toward five o'clock. He swung his gun forward, and then he saw it. The outside engine was on fire.

"Jerry! Number Four's on fire! It's on fire!" he yelled.

Jerry opened the extinguisher and, at the same time, he turned the *Harpy* over to Story. "She's yours, Story!"

A moment later, Pon yelled, "She's out! She's out," he repeated softly, and the words held a quiet terror. The engine was dead.

John threw the mask from his face. They were getting down now. An eager, violent anger shook him, as if it had been long awaited. His anger did not spring from the terrible fire that exploded upward, the horrible cracking of the air. It was something deeper and stronger and more impersonal. Looking downward, it seemed that the roads of Ohio should be running there. All his life he had known the open, wide roads and searched them. He had smelled their tar and cement and sand and clay, the white schoolhouses and the whiter churches. He had asked for rides and given them. There was no freedom in the world like the freedom of America and her roads. It seemed that it would be drowned beneath him, and he screamed in bitter challenge. He screamed again and again, as if, when eternity quieted all things, the sound of his outraged voice would still be heard.

Jerry waited. He was helplessly overcome by a desire to strike something with all his might. He knew he was cool. He knew everything that was happening. He had to make the decision in a moment. In just one second more it had to be made. We can't warn the convoy, he thought. It's too late. They don't keep up contact. They can't. They'd give themselves away. Tomorrow morning they are coming in, and they'll be slaughtered. They'll be drained of blood in the beguiling water. They should be climbing the beach, crossing the island, clearing it, grasping victory quickly. But they won't. Not if the *Harpy* returns home.

"Story, save half of them!" he called sharply. "We'll get those boats!"

He leaned forward, his nerves as alert as if they were held on the blade of a shining scalpel. He felt no need to hurry, to force the ship. She was moving to her goal.

Story leaned forward, his fingers cool and flexible. He adjusted the sight as carefully as a musician adjusts his instrument. The *Harpy* pulled heavily. Her dead engine weighed on her wing. Come on, girlie, he begged. Come on, *Harpy*.

They were racing up the edge of the beach now. The fire was bursting below him as if he were just a little to the left. He moved her slowly, his head cocked as a violinist listens to his tuning.

"Bomb bays open!"

Now, come along, girlie; come along to the *Darktown Strutters' Ball*. The rhythm was wonderful in his mind and fingers, marking the time as the earth rushed beneath them, rushed backward, drawing the target into his sight.

"Bombs away!"

Jerry and Watts grabbed the *Harpy*. The ships were anchored about three miles down the reef, and along every inch of the lagoon ack-ack shoved upward.

"Norry! John! Keep your eyes open!"

"Right!" John shouted, and waited for Norry's voice. It did not come.

"Norry, Norry!" he called, and then he slipped his intercom loose and flung himself back through the ship. It smelled hot, like a radiator without water in it, and oily. He put his hand against the side next to the life raft, and the jagged holes gouged his fingers.

Ahead of him, he saw Norry slumped in his seat. He crawled to him, calling, "Norry, Norry, did they get you?" and then his voice trailed off. Norry sat there, quietly erect, a piece of enemy shrapnel in his hand. John lifted him out of the turret and carried him deeper into the ship.

Krist was the only one who could handle Norry's gun now. John hurried forward. The air rushed up through the open bomb bays, tearing at his clothing, and below him, on either side of the narrow catwalk, he saw the land moving dimly beneath the dark erupting smoke. Blood was running down Krist's face and across the front of his dislodged mask.

Krist opened his eyes slightly, as if he had never opened them wider. "John, drive them into the water. Blow them up," he whispered hoarsely, and his eyes closed.

John raised himself slowly, looking down at Krist. There was something unstrained and happy in the face. The whole face was gentle and sensitive now.

Turning, he started the trip back across the bomb bay. He walked almost slowly. That was it. He had almost known it all the time. He had known it since that afternoon on the road in Ohio. They had forgotten what America meant, and those who became alert quickest, fought quickest, sacrificed readily. It was as simple and right and inevitable as that, he realized.

Pon grabbed him as he walked by, shaking him. "Take the tail!" Pon shouted. "I'll handle these!" He nodded at the two waist guns, and then shouted into the intercom, "Jerry, Norry is gone! Norry is out!"

Jerry did not answer. He was pushing with all his weight and all his might at some terrible burning thing that caught in his stomach. He forced his weight down on his feet until his body shoved itself against the safety straps, and then suddenly the release came and he fell back. It felt good and clean, as if he had been plunged into cool water. The air rushing through the splintered plastic felt wonderful, only it was smoky. They were going out over the water. I must be tired, he thought. Sleepy. It was smoky and cool, like an autumn night, like the one when he had met Betts, and he was sleepy, deeply and gratefully sleepy, for the release was coming now.

Watts did not have time to more than glance at him. The target was out in front—two heavy barriers, crowded and threatening. They alone held meaning, and the *Harpy* descended on them as if she barely needed his guidance.

"Story, Jerry is out," he said quietly. "We're going down low. Lay them on the decks."

"Take the big one first," Story said. "Then we'll cross the stern on the other one."

In the belly turret, it seemed to Walt that the ships were flinging themselves upward from the water. Hundreds of men, small but growing larger, scrambled about.

"I've got her!" Story shouted.

Watts let her ride.

Pon turned his gun downward, starting a spray toward the deck. Men dropped from the debarking net, leaped from the decks, flinging their equipment wildly.

Walt saw the two bombs free themselves and then spin downward. He watched them even in the moment when they struck the deck and the deep port side. Then the whole ship exploded, and then exploded again and again. Ammunition, he thought, as the *Harpy* lunged forward, rocked by the tremendous concussion.

Watts pulled on the *Harpy*. She banked awkwardly, pulled around and headed for the other ship. They were down now, not more than eight hundred feet from the water.

Mike waited in the top turret, looking into the exploded

skies. The formation behind them was just coming in. According to plan, the *Harpy* should be far down over the lagoon, but as she neared the second ship, Mike could look ahead and see the thousand-pounders heading downward for the gun emplacements. He glanced up at the Liberators again. It seemed that they were tremendously high and that the *Harpy* would never get up there again. He did not think there was any power in the world that could lift her back into the heavens.

Chief stared ahead at the superstructure of the boat. He wondered if they would clear it. It didn't matter much any longer. He did not think he could summon the strength to lift his head from the base of the gun, anyway. As the light came down on his brown face, Chief recalled the fires he had built as a child, the cool canyons, the mesquite and pine nuts, the places he had seen in America. Rich and sturdy and endlessly giving, this America had always been. But now, thinking of America, his face held compassion and love, quiet nobility and unknown strength. All these were deep in the lines of his face, but they were brushed across by a quiet serenity and peace. He rested his head, thinking of the wonderful years in which his people had known their country, the seasons which had passed, the autumns and springs they had known, the fierce winters and the last end of summer which had taken their name. The Creator had said there was a season for everything. "A time to love, and a time to hate; a time of war, and a time of peace." In all history of man's growth these words had been true. And now his time was here, Chief knew—the time of war.

"Here we go!" Story shouted, and he shoved all the

bombs free. He couldn't miss, he knew. It was like dropping rocks off a bridge. He turned to grab the thirty-calibers beside him, but as he got to his knees, the whole world seemed to shatter before him. Everything broke with a brilliant, crystal clarity, cracking into new shapes, as intricate and beautiful as hoarfrost, and he just sat down easily and smiled. It's not so bad, he kept telling himself. It's not so bad, only the wind comes in so strongly. If there just wasn't the wind to take my breath away. Or perhaps it wasn't the wind.

As he touched his body, he knew there was no place the spattering shrapnel hadn't cut its way.

"Whatever they give you to do, I want you to be happy, remembering."

The light came back, the glorious luminous light in the shrine in the cathedral that always remained after the red and blues and greens had become harsh and dissolved in the brash morning. The luminous light remained always.

Watts tried to anticipate the explosion. He tried to bank the *Harpy* a little, so she wouldn't catch it full force against her wings. He was afraid they'd snap off. But just as he banked, it hit her, driving her downward and forward.

Walt felt the concussion, saw the black cloud of smoke surround him, and out of it the leaping dull-red flames with the brilliant orange tongues. They encircled him, and for a moment he thought the turret would melt. He flung his arm across his face, felt the force of the blow throw him about the turret, and then he was grasping for something to steady himself. The turret was turned downward, and he faced directly toward the water. It was only about a hundred feet below him, and they were losing altitude rapidly. The whitecaps were rushing up toward him. He watched them come up. It seemed that he could almost touch them.

Watts felt the sweat all over his body. It was cold, as if he sat with his body clamped in wet towels. We should be hitting any second, he told himself, and he kept yanking and pulling. He kept hoping the *Harpy* would find enough air to hold onto and pull herself up from the surface of the ocean.

"No, *Harpy,* no!" Pon shouted. None of them who could still move made any effort to leave the ship. Pon would not. He had never pictured the *Harpy's* end, but he knew it wasn't here. It wasn't in a whirling, exploded bay, where the debris still rained down from the skies.

She held. She held as if her very wing tips were caught on the edge of some unseen support. Watts flung himself forward, working with the engine. Suddenly, the Number Four caught. The right wing pulled down a little, leveled, and they roared forward into the billowing black smoke. She was riding now. Watts could feel her under his hands. She had taken on life. He turned as sharply as he dared with the speed they had, and started back out across the exploded ships. He had to get out to sea and get some speed. It was the only hope.

Looking down, Walt saw the larger of the two Nip ships slowly tumble on its side and roll over as if it had become unbalanced. Equipment and men were thrown free into the air and downward onto the burning water. The other ship sat quiet and fat, like a child's bath toy, only the flames roared upward for better than a hundred feet. The infantry and marines and all the others could come in now. The resistance was broken. The winds of America could blow westward as they had in Kula Gulf and Kahili and Munda and Midway, Guadalcanal and Makin and Tarawa. The season of war would soon be gone, and there would be the season of peace.

Slowly and purposefully, the *Harpy* gained altitude. She was climbing toward some secret place. Mike jumped down to look at Krist, and it was in that moment the fighters came down from above. Two of them came out of the billowing smoke clouds, and only John saw them. He grabbed his gun and began to fire. He was unused to the tail turret, and he knew he was going wild. His hands were steady and his guns were spitting cartridges with the neat rapidity of a sewing machine, but he knew it was coming. The Zekes crossed just above the *Harpy,* and their fire left an X seamed across her fuselage. Mike ripped into the one going off to his left and held his fire on her, until something heavier than a hammer struck his arm and knocked it away from the gun.

He took the handkerchief he always wore around his neck and stuffed it down the sleeve of his suit. He could feel the warm blood down there, but it wasn't hurting him much. It was then, as he turned back to his gun, that he saw Jerry slumped sideways in his seat. He crawled up beside him and felt his forehead. It was warm, he thought, but he couldn't be sure. Everything was warm, the fume-filled air was sticky with oily, smoky heat. Unsnapping the belt, he lifted Jerry easily and carried him back beside Krist. He laid him on the platform and turned back to Watts. It was then he saw the fighter coming in at two o'clock, straight ahead of them, and its whole wing edge seemed to be ablaze with firing guns.

Watts opened his eyes a little and looked up. "Take it! Take it, Mike. I—"

Mike saw that one of the bullets had ripped along the edge of Watts' head, and blood was pouring down around his ear. Mike fell into the pilot's seat. His hands and legs stopped stiffly, helplessly. He looked at the things he thought must be done, but he was helpless to move. The *Harpy* was riding into a cloud bank that rested above the ocean's surface. She was climbing quickly, and before he realized it, the cloud flooded in around them, blotting out the disaster they had left, obstructing everything that lay ahead. Mike started to reach for the throttles, but paused again.

Just then, something moved beside him, and he turned to see Pon. Mike did not know how he had been warned, but there he stood, straight and thin, his face whiter than Mike had ever seen it. But it wasn't fear that made it white, or anger, or any emotion that Mike had ever known. It was white as if it had always been that way, and it was calm.

Without speaking, Pon lifted Watts gently from the co-pilot's seat and placed him back of them on the flight deck. Unhurried, as if now more than ever in their lives there was no need to hurry, no cause to be concerned with time. It was curious how dreamlike were the movements of men when they were timeless. Mike stared at him. It seemed as if he had never known him before. And yet he was not sure. There was some curious recognition in his face. Pon reached for the controls. It was then that Mike noticed how thin his hands were and how he held them, the fingers partially bent in a sort of repose.

It seemed a long while that they rode through the dark, rain-filled cloud. The fuselage of the *Harpy* hummed with the rain, but it no longer held terror for them. It was a soothing, gentle, and unending sound, and beneath Pon's hands, from some unmeasurable source, she drew strength. She sang as if time and space were unlimited to her. New and untried air pushed up against her wings, and when the cloud fell away, she was high in the sky.

Mike leaned back, his eyes closed against the wind that poured through the shattered plane. This was what he had always dreamed of—this quiet riding in the valley of the sky.

A sweet serenity spread over him, and he felt a completeness within himself, and yet this was part of a continuity, he knew. This was the end for which the beginning had been made; this was the beginning for which the end had been promised.

The sun had fallen away over the horizon, far down across the earth. It flung a shaft of light upward. The vaulted space between the dark cloud and shaft was golden, and colored all the heavens about it. The shaft rose upward into infinite space, passing through the deep and distant blue, and into that shaft the *Harpy* climbed easily, moving unhindered, like some great homing bird.

The sound of her motors sang through the heavens, clear and loud and endless. They sang through the sunset and into the darkness. Long after midnight, and in the midnights to follow, her ground crew, lying on the mat with their eyes in the starry distance, believed they heard the sound of the *Harpy*'s singing. But they did not speak of it, for all men who ride on the wings of the heavens listen for the *Harpy*, knowing her spirit was infinite.

The Beaches of Dunkirk

"BARTIMEUS"

The evacuation of the British Expeditionary Force from the fire-swept coast of France, from Calais to the beaches of La Panne, from which the British and French navies embarked 335,000 troops and carried them to safety, has been described as a miracle; and certain factors of chance did undoubtedly operate in the Allies' favor. Calm seas and occasional mist on certain days were an advantage. But wherein lay the miracle was the degree of stubborn courage attained by hundreds of thousands of quite ordinary men. Mere leadership, mere skill in organization, could have achieved nothing without this mass resistance to the fear of death and an unconquerable belief in ultimate victory. The tale of human valor outlines the causes that gave it birth, whether they are victories or reverses. The world's tragedy is that war brings it to its most splendid flower.

The yacht-club telephone rang, and the elderly steward, unaccustomed to the sound of it, laid down his paper, removed his spectacles, and picked up the receiver. A man's voice spoke authoritatively for about a minute.

The steward said nothing. He was an old Navy man and had been a pensioner for a quarter of a century, but he recognized the note in the speaker's voice. He waited till the end of the message.

"Aye, aye, sir," he said, and then added, "there's only the one yacht here now, sir. The *Wanderer*. Motor yacht, forty feet long. There's no crew, sir. Owner's fighting in France. There's a young lady on board at this moment—"

The voice interrupted him. He listened, turning the spectacles over in his knotted fingers, staring into vacancy.

"Aye, aye, sir. I'll do what I can. Old Navy man myself. They said I was too old to fight."

There was no answer. "Hello, sir?" Silence. He replaced the receiver.

The *Wanderer* was lying at her buoy, and there was no sign of the girl. He untied the dinghy lying at the jetty and rowed alongside. At the sound of the oars as he boated them, the girl's head and shoulders appeared above the companionway. She was flushed and had a scrubbing brush in her hand.

"They want her, miss," he said simply. "They rung up from the Admiralty. Proceed to Ramsgate for orders. They're taking every craft on the south coast."

She brushed a lock of hair back from her damp forehead with her forearm. "I'm single-handed," she said. "Can you run the engine if I steer?"

"You, miss?" He hadn't thought of that.

"She's full up with petrol. There's water, too, and some stuff in tins to eat. Bring some bread."

"You know what it's for, don't you, miss? They won't let a woman—"

"They needn't know," was the girl's answer. She stood motionless, thinking. The ebb tide running past the strakes of the dinghy made a little chuckling noise in the stillness.

"Bring a couple of shrapnel helmets. Get them from the A.R.P. people. What about Johnnie?"

"Johnnie?" He turned that over in his mind. Johnnie was simple, but he was useful in a boat. Ashore he just sat and played with pebbles, but put him in a boat and he was all there. The club employed him to ferry people to their yachts and for attending to the moorings, and odd jobs like scraping and painting. He didn't speak very plain, but after all it wasn't talk they wanted on the beaches of Dunkirk. Another aspect of the situation occurred to him. She seemed to take it for granted he was coming. "What about the club, miss? I'm the caretaker *and* steward."

She had emerged from her reverie. "The club? What does the club matter?"

He grinned, showing tobacco-stained teeth. "You've said it, miss. Give me half an hour."

When he was halfway across to the jetty, she hailed him again. Her clear voice was like a boy's. "Johnnie will want a shrapnel helmet too."

He nodded; she went below and fell to mopping up the mess on the cabin floor. She had decided to give the boat a scrubout because it occupied her mind, which, since she had had no word from France for three weeks, was inclined to imagine things. This was where they had spent the happiest hours of his leave—the happiest hours of their lives. And now, for all she knew, he was waiting on those hellish beaches, one of all those thousands of exhausted men, waiting under shell and machine-gun fire for succor from England. She flung the mop and scrubber into the bucket and jerked open a drawer. There was all his old kit: gray flannel trousers, sweater, an old shooting jacket, a yellow muffler. She would push her hair up under the shrapnel helmet. His pipes stuck in a rack over his bunk caught her eye. That would be the finishing touch. Keep one of those in her mouth when they got to Ramsgate, and talk gruff. She selected a blackened bulldog and experimented in front of the glass. It tasted utterly foul.

Coming down channel, they overtook a convoy of motor yachts and followed them. She had the chart open in front of her, but the daylight was fading and there were no lights anywhere she could recognize. She had never entered Ramsgate from seaward—only from the railway station, once as a child, carrying her doll and a spade and bucket, in the charge of her nurse.

She listened to the drone of the engine with satisfaction. Old Ferris had been a mechanic when he served in the Navy. It wasn't so good at the start, but he was enjoying himself down in the engine room now he had picked up the hang of the thing. Every now and again he put his head out of the hatch with his spectacles on the end of his nose. "Running as sweet as a nut, miss," he announced.

"Bravo," she answered.

Johnnie sat in the bows staring at the evening star. She tried to remember why she had brought Johnnie. He worshiped her like a dog, but that wasn't the reason. It was because she felt she had no right to take an able-bodied man from his work in England; and on the spur of the moment she could think of nobody on the spot who was as handy in the boat. He and she used to take Johnnie away for the week end sometimes. Johnnie washed up and looked after the boat when they went ashore. She was one of the few people who understood what he said. He turned his head and smiled at her at that moment. It was the slow, confiding smile of a child. He hadn't the remotest idea where he was going. He didn't care. He just trusted her. She felt a swift pang of compunction, and stifled it, giving him back his smile. Reassured, he resumed his contemplation of the star.

She climbed ashore in the dusk, the awful pipe clenched between her teeth, and was confronted by a man in the uniform of a lieutenant commander.

"What ship?"

"*Wanderer.*" Nobody had ever called the *Wanderer* a ship before. He would have liked that.

"What is she?"

"Forty-foot motor cruiser."

"Armed?"

She shook her head. Other owners of yachts were crowding around asking for orders.

He glanced at her shrapnel helmet.

"Well, you'd better collect some rifles and life belts. First-aid outfit, too, if you haven't got it."

"Then what?" She stuck her hands in her trouser pockets, making her voice as gruff and laconic as possible.

"La Panne. Time it so as to get there in the dawn. Take off all you've got room for each trip and transfer them to something bigger. Stick it as long as you can, and good luck." He indicated a gap in the barbed wire, where she supposed rifles and life belts were obtainable, and dismissed her from his mind.

She went back to the edge of the jetty and hailed old Ferris. The harbor was crammed with dim forms of boats maneuvering for berths alongside. Beside her on the pier-head was a soldier with a Bren gun mounted on a tripod.

"Ferris," she called down to the *Wanderer*, "come ashore with me and collect some rifles and life belts." The soldier sidled up beside her.

"Here, Skipper," he muttered, "rifles ain't no use. Take me and this Bren gun. Wait till it's dark and I'll slip down and come along with you. They won't miss me till I'm back."

She grinned delightedly. He would know about rifles, too. She had never fired one in her life. "All right," she whispered. "What's your name?"

"Tanner's the name, Skipper. You're a sport." She felt a bit of a sport.

To the westward the oil tanks of Dunkirk were a sullen blaze that every now and again leaped upward like the eruption of a volcano as a shell burst in the flaming inferno. Fires glowed dully along the coast, and shore batteries blinked white flashes that reached the ear as dull reverberations like distant thunder. The searchlights wheeled about the low-flying clouds into which tracer shells were soaring.

They had solved the problem of navigating to La Panne by following a paddle steamer that had half a dozen lifeboats in tow. The whole night was full of the sound of motorboats' exhausts. There was a young moon peeping in and out of the drifting clouds, and it revealed the indistinct lines of little craft far and wide, heading in the same direction.

Johnnie sat entranced by the spectacle, crowing huskily at intervals. Tanner, having mounted his Bren gun in the stern, gave her a relief at the wheel. He said it was much the same as driving a car. She practiced loading the rifle under his tuition. Old Ferris visited them at intervals, calling her "Skipper." It didn't matter what Johnnie called her, because nobody could understand what he said.

"You're a bit young for this game, eh, Skipper?" asked Tanner. "How old are you?"

"About a hundred," she replied with a gruff laugh. And in that moment, before the dawn of hell's delight, she felt it.

The dawn came slowly, revealing the small craft of the south coast of England covering the Channel like water beetles on the surface of a pool. Pleasure steamers and yachts, barges, scoots, wherries, lifeboats, motorboats, rowing boats, and canoes. Fishermen, yachtsmen, longshoremen, men who had never been afloat in their lives, millionaires and the very poor, elderly men and lads in their teens, answering in a headlong rush the appeal for boats. Boats for the beaches and the last of the Expeditionary Force.

Somehow she hadn't thought about the dead. Her thoughts were entirely occupied with the living. It wasn't till Johnnie began making queer noises of distress and pointing down into the shallow water that she saw them—the men who had been machine-gunned in the shallows, wading out into the water to reach security. They were still there, some floating, some submerged; in an odd way they seemed to convey resentment at the disturbance of their oblivion by the passing keels.

She called Johnnie to her side. "Take the lead line and sound over the bows. Call the soundings. Nothing else matters. Do you understand, Johnnie? Nothing else matters. I am here."

He made guttural noises, pointing at Tanner, who was blazing away with the Bren gun at a Heinkel overhead that had bombed a trawler astern of them. She held him with her eyes. "Nothing else matters, do you understand?" He picked up the lead line and went forward obediently. She put her lips to the voice pipe. "Go very slow, Ferris."

"Go very slow," repeated the old man.

She crept inshore. The beach was pitted with shell craters

out of which men came running, wading out into the water to meet them. From the sand dunes more men stumbled, helping the wounded. The whole foreshore was alive with men and boats, and the smoke from the Dunkirk fires flowed over them like a dark river.

At three and a half feet she would stop. It was the least they could float in. She listened to the strange cries Johnnie emitted as he hauled in the dripping lead line, understanding them perfectly.

Presently, her mouth to the voice pipe, she gave the order to stop. Tanner was having trouble with the Bren gun and swearing in a ceaseless flow of incomprehensible blasphemy. Old Ferris, complete in shrapnel helmet and life belt, climbed out of his hatch and came toward her, lighting his pipe.

"They said I was too old to fight, but—"

"Get back. We're in four feet. I must keep working the engines." A bomb burst among the men wading toward them. She shut her eyes for a moment. "Keep on sounding, Johnnie. What water have you got?"

"Fraghfaph-ah-ah," crowed Johnnie.

"Good boy. Keep it going."

The Bren gun broke out afresh. Tanner, having cleared the jam, opened fire again, chanting oaths like a denunciatory psalm. "Slow astern, Ferris."

Another cluster of men wading to their armpits had reached them.

Johnnie looked back at her and pointed at their sun-scorched, puffing faces. No doubt existed in his mind that it was all something to do with his lead-line achievements. He was delighted. Somewhere out of sight a German field-gun battery opened fire, the shells whistling viciously overhead.

She searched every face as they came splashing and gasping toward her and somehow contrived to hoist each other inboard. She took sixty or seventy at a trip and transferred them to the nearest vessel lying out in the deep water; she had hitherto believed that the utmost capacity of the *Wanderer* was a dozen. Backward and forward they went under exploding bombs, under machine-gun fire and whining shells. Tanner ran out of ammunition and they went alongside a destroyer, where he got another case and a spare barrel for the Bren gun. She lost all count of time, all fear, all feeling. Sometimes she interrogated weary men: Had they seen his unit? Had they ever heard his name? They shook their heads and begged for water. She had none left.

Then suddenly it seemed that the beaches were empty. She didn't know that the men were being marched westward to Dunkirk, where the French and British destroyers were crowding alongside the mole and embarking troops in thousands under shellfire. Except for a few scattered units moving west, the beaches were empty. The task was done; but where was he—where was he?

The Bren gun had been silent for a long time, but she hadn't noticed. Now, turning to look seaward, she saw Tanner lying beside it with his knees screwed up into his belly. She ran aft and knelt beside him.

His eyes sought hers out of his gray face. "I bought it, Skipper. Sorry. . . . Got a drop of water?"

She raised his head and held it against her breast. "There isn't any water left."

His eyes were suddenly puzzled. He moved his head sideways a little and then smiled, and died, ineffably content.

They followed a big gray coaster back to Dover. Old Ferris got a spare red ensign out of the locker and tucked Tanner up in it. He didn't mind Tanner's being killed, having been disposed to regard him jealously as an intruder into a nice little family party. Moreover, he disapproved of his language. He walked forward to the wheelhouse. She was moving the spokes of the wheel slowly between her blistered hands. Her shrapnel helmet lay on the chart beside the valiant briar pipe. She was aware of the old man beside her and of having reached the end of her tether at one and the same moment.

Old Ferris kicked Johnnie, asleep at her feet, into wakefulness. "Take the wheel," he said gruffly, and held her as she pitched, sobbing and exhausted, into his arms.

They berthed alongside the Admiralty pier, and she climbed ashore to find someone who could give them fuel and water. The quays were thronged with troops in thousands, being fed and sorted out into units and entrained. A hospital ship was evacuating wounded into fleets of ambulances. She stepped aside to give room to the bearers of a stretcher and glanced at the face on the pillow.

He had a bandage around his head and opened his eyes suddenly on her face.

"I've been looking for you," she announced in a calm matter-of-fact tone. She felt no emotion whatever.

He smiled. "Well, here I am," he said.

The Young Man from Kalgoorlie

H. E. BATES

He lived with his parents on a sheep farm two hundred miles northeast of Kalgoorlie. The house was in the old style, a simple white wooden cabin to which a few extensions had been added by successive generations. On the low hills east of the farm there were a few eucalyptus trees; his mother grew pink and mauve asters under the house windows in summer; and in spring the wattle was in blossom everywhere, like lemon foam. All of his life had been lived there, and the war itself was a year old before he knew that it had even begun.

On the bomber station, surrounded by flat gray English hills cropped mostly by sugar beet and potatoes and steeped in wintertime in thick windless fogs that kept the aircraft grounded for days at a time, he used to tell me how it had come to happen that he did not know the war had started. It seemed he used to go down to Kalgoorlie only once, perhaps twice, a year. I do not know what sort of place Kalgoorlie is, but it seemed that he did there, on that one visit or so, all the things that anyone can do on a visit to almost any town in the world. He used to take a room for a week at a hotel, get up at what he thought was a late hour every morning—about eight o'clock—and spend most of the day looking at shops, eating, and then looking at shops again. In the evenings he used to take in a cinema, eat another meal, have a couple of glasses of beer in the hotel lounge, and then go to bed. He confessed that it wasn't very exciting, and often he was relieved to get back into the Ford and drive steadily back to the sheep farm and the familiar horizon of eucalyptus trees, which after the streets of Kalgoorlie did not seem a bad prospect at all. The truth was that he did not know anyone in Kalgoorlie except an aunt, his mother's sister, who was very deaf and used a patent electrical acoustic device, which always seemed to go wrong whenever he was there and which he had once spent more than a day trying to repair. He was very quiet, and he did not easily get mixed up with people; he was never drunk, and more than half the time he was worried that his father was making a mess of things at home.

It was this that was really the cause of his not knowing about the war. His father was an unimaginative and rather careless man to whom sheep were simply sheep, and grass simply grass, and who had kept sheep on the same two thousand acres, within sight of the same eucalyptus trees for thirty years, and expected to go on keeping them there for the rest of his life. He did not understand that two years of bad luck had anything to do with his having kept sheep in the same way, on the same grass, for so long. It was the son who discovered that. He began to see that the native grasses were played out, and in their place he decided to make sowings of Italian rye grass and subterranean clover; and soon he was able to change the flocks from one kind of grass to another and then on to a third, and soon he could see an improvement in the health of every breed they had.

After that he was virtually in charge of the farm. His parents, who had always thought him a wonderful person, now thought him more wonderful still. When neighbors came—and this, too, was not often, since the nearest farm was another thirty miles up country—they talked of nothing but Albert's achievement. The sheep had improved in health, the yield of wool had increased, and even the mutton, they argued, tasted sweeter now, more like the meat of thirty years ago. "Got a proper old-fashioned flavor," his mother said.

It was about a year after these experiments of his—none of them very original, since he had simply read up on the whole subject in an agricultural paper—that war broke out. It seemed, as he afterward found out, that his mother first heard of it on an early-morning news bulletin on the radio. She was scared and she called his father. The son himself was out on the farm, riding around on horseback taking a look at the sheep before breakfast. When he came in to breakfast he switched on the radio, but nothing happened. He opened up the radio and took a look at it. All the valves were warm, but the detector valve and another were not operating. It seemed a little odd, but he did not take much notice of it. All he could do was write to Kalgoorlie for the spare valves, and he did so in a letter which he wrote after dinner that day. It was three miles to the postbox, and if there were any letters to be posted his mother took them down in the afternoon. His mother took this letter that afternoon and tore it up in little pieces.

That must have happened, he discovered, to every letter he wrote to the Kalgoorlie radio shop in the next twelve months. No valves ever came and gradually, since it was summer and sheep-shearing time and the busiest season of the year, the family got used to being without the radio. His father and mother said they even preferred it. All the time he had no idea of the things they were doing in order to keep the war from him. The incoming post arrived once a week, and if there were any letters for him, his mother steamed them open, read them, and then put the dangerous ones away in a drawer upstairs. The newspapers stopped coming, and when he remarked on it his father said he was tired of wasting good money on papers that were anyway nearly a week old before they came. If there were visitors his mother managed to meet them before they reached the house. In October the sheep-shearing contractors came, and his father, ordinarily a rather careful man, gave every man an extra pound to keep his mouth shut. All through that summer and the following winter his mother looked very ill, but it was not until later that he knew the reason of it—the strain of intercepting the letters, of constantly guarded conversation, of warning neighbors and callers, of making excuses, and even of lying to him, day after day, for almost a year.

The time came when he decided to go to Kalgoorlie. He always went there about the same time of the year, in late August, before the busy season started. His parents must have anticipated and dreaded that moment, and his father did an amazing thing. In the third week of August, early one morning, he put two tablespoonfuls of salt in a cup of hot tea and drank it, making himself very sick. By the time Albert came in to breakfast, his father was back in bed, very yellow in the face, and his mother was crying because he had been taken suddenly ill. It was the strangest piece of deception of all, and it might have succeeded if his father had not overdone things. He decided to remain in bed for a second week, making himself sick every third or fourth day, knowing that once September had come, Albert would never leave. But Albert was worried. He did not like the recurrent sickness which now affected his father, and he began to fear some sort of internal trouble.

"I'm going to Kalgoorlie whether you like it or not," he said, "to get a doctor."

It was on the bomber station, when he had become a pilot, that he used to tell me of that first day in Kalgoorlie, one of the most remarkable in his life. When he left the farm his mother seemed very upset, and began crying. He felt that she was worried about his father; he was increasingly worried too and promised to be back within three days. Then he drove down to Kalgoorlie alone, perhaps the only man in Australia who did not know that the war was a year old.

He arrived at Kalgoorlie about four o'clock in the afternoon, and the town seemed much the same as ever. He drove straight to the hotel he always stayed at, booked himself a room, and went upstairs to wash and change. About five o'clock he came down again and went into the hotel lounge for a cup of tea. Except for a word or two with the cashier and the lift boy he did not speak to a soul. He finished his tea and then decided to go to the downstairs saloon, as he always did, to get himself a haircut. There were several people waiting in the saloon, but he decided to wait too. He sat down and picked up a paper.

He must have gone on staring at that paper, not really reading it, for about ten minutes. It was late August and the Nazis were bombing London. He did not understand any of it—who was fighting or what were the causes of it. He simply took in, from the headlines, the story of the great sky battles, the bombing, the murder and destruction, as if they were part of a ghastly fantasy. For the moment he did not feel angry or sick or outraged because he had been deceived. He got up and went out into the street. What he felt, he told me, was very much as if you were suddenly to discover that you had been living in a house where, without knowing it, there was a carrier of smallpox. For months you have lived an ordinary tranquil life, unsuspecting and unafraid, and then suddenly you made the awful discovery that every fragment of your life, from the dust in your shoes to the air you breathed, was contaminated and that you had been living in danger. Because you knew nothing you were not afraid; but the moment you knew anything all the fears and terrors you had not felt in the past were precipitated into a single terrible moment of realization.

He also felt a fool. He walked up and down the street. As he passed shops, read placards, saw men in service uniform, fragmentary parts of his life during the past year became joined together, making sense: the broken radio, his unanswered letters, the newspapers, his mother's nervousness, and the fact, above all, that they had not wanted him to come to Kalgoorlie. Slowly he understood all this. He tried to look on it as the simple cunning of country people. He was still too confused to be angry. But what he still did not understand, and what he had to find out about soon was the war. He did not even know how long it had been going on. He stopped on a street corner and bought another newspaper. The day before, he read, eighty-seven aircraft had been shot down over England. His hands were trembling as he read it, but it did not tell him the things he wanted to know. And he realized suddenly, as he stood there trembling in the hot sunshine, so amazed that he was still without feeling, that there was no means of knowing these things. He certainly could not know by asking. He imagined the effect of asking anyone, in the street or the hotel or back in the barber's saloon, a simple question like, "Can you tell me when the war began?" He felt greatly oppressed by a sense of ridicule and bewilderment, by the fear that now, any time he opened his mouth, he was likely to make a ghastly fool of himself.

He walked about for an hour or more, pretending to look

at shops, before it occurred to him what to do. Then it came to him quite suddenly that he would go and see the only other person he knew who, like himself, could be cut off from the world of reality—the deaf aunt who lived in Kalgoorlie.

So he spent most of that evening in the old-fashioned parlor of her house, drinking tea, eating custard tarts, lightly browned with veins of nutmeg, and talking as steadily as he could into the electrical acoustic device fixed to the bodice of her dress. From such remarks as, "Things look pretty tough in England. Let's see, how long exactly has it been going on now?" he learned most of the elementary things he wanted to know. But there were still things he could not ask, simply because he had no knowledge of them. He could not ask about France or Poland or Holland or Norway. All that he really understood clearly was that England and Germany were at war; that England was being bombed every day by great forces of aircraft; that soon, perhaps, she would be invaded. The simplicity and limitation of his knowledge were in a way, as he said, a good thing. For as he ate the last of the old lady's custard tarts and drank the last cup of tea and said good night to her, he changed from being the man who knew least about the war in all Australia to the man who had perhaps the clearest, simplest, and most vivid conception of it in the whole continent. Forty years back his father and mother had emigrated from Lincolnshire to Kalgoorlie. Young, newly wed, and with about eighty pounds apart from their passage money, they started a new life. Now the roots of their existence, and so in a way the roots of his own existence, were being threatened with annihilation. This was the clear, simple, terrible thing he understood in such a clear, simple, terrible way.

When he got back to his hotel he drafted a telegram to his parents, telling them, as well as he could, that he understood. Then in the morning he went around to the nearest recruiting center. I have not so far described what he was like. He was rather tall, fair, and brown in the face; his eyes were a cool blue and his lips thin, determined, and rather tight. He was just twenty-two, and he had no way of holding back his anger.

"I want to be a pilot," he said.

"All right," they said. "Good. But you can't be a pilot all of a sudden, just like that."

"No?" he said. "No? We'll soon see."

He adjusted himself as time went on, but he carried some of his first angry, clear, terrible conceptions of things across the sea—across the Pacific to Vancouver, across the Atlantic to England. He was never angry with his parents, and they in turn ceased being afraid about him. He used to describe to me how he went home on his first leave. From being stupidly affectionate in one way about him they became stupidly affectionate in quite another. They had not wanted him to go; now, because he had gone, they behaved as if they had everything to do with sending him and nothing to do with keeping him away. They had arranged a party, and he said it was the largest gathering of folks anyone had ever seen on the farm. They invited everyone for thirty miles around and one or two people from fifty miles away. They killed several spring lambs and about fifteen fowls, and tea was brewing all day long. At night they sang hymns and old songs in the drawing room around the piano, and they slept on the floor. In the end he was almost glad to get away.

He promised to write to them often, and he promised also to keep a diary. He always did write, and he always kept the diary. He sailed for Vancouver early in the year, and by the spring he was flying Ansons and by the summer he was in England. It was an uncertain and rather treacherous summer, and the harvest was wet and late in the corn country where we were. The potato fields were blighted, so that they looked as if they were spattered by drops of coffee on the dark rainy autumn days, and for long periods low clouds kept the aircraft down. Gradually the harvest fields were cleaned and the potatoes sacked and carted away, and in place of them you could see pale golden cones of sugar beet piled in the fields and by the roadsides. I mention the weather, because it was almost the only thing about England that troubled him. He longed for the hot dry air of the Australian summer, and he used to tell me, as we gazed over the wet flat country, of the days when he had flown over Victoria in a Moth in his shirt sleeves and had looked down on the white beaches shining all along the coast in the sun.

The weather troubled him because his anger was still there. He felt that it frustrated him. He could never forget the day in Kalgoorlie when he had first read of the bombing and the mass murder in England, and the very headlines of the paper had seemed like an awful dream. He felt that so much of his life had still to be brought up to date. Something had to be vindicated. Yet you could never tell that he was angry. It was easier to tell that he was sometimes afraid;

not that he was afraid of dying or being hurt, but of some material thing like mishandling a plane. As he graduated from Moths to Ansons, to Blenheims and Wellingtons, and finally to Stirlings, he felt each time that he would never be big enough for the change to the bigger aircraft, yet it was always because of that fear that he was big enough.

Late that autumn he became captain of a Stirling, and about the same time he got to know a girl. Two or three evenings a week, if there were no operations, we used to go down into the town and drink a few glasses of beer at a pub called the Grenadier, and one evening this girl came in. She was very dark and rather sophisticated, with very red lips, and she never wore her coat in the ordinary way, but simply had it slung on her shoulders, with the sleeves empty and dangling. "This is Olivia," he said. For some reason I never knew her other name; we most often called her Albert's popsy, but after that, every night we were in the Grenadier, she would come in, and soon, after talking for a time, they would go off somewhere alone together. The weather was very bad at that time and he saw her quite often. And then for a few nights it cleared, and one night, before going over to Bremen, he asked if I would keep his date with her and make his apologies and explain.

He had arranged to see her at seven o'clock, and I made a bad impression by being late and because, above all, I was the wrong person.

"Don't be angry," I said. "I'm very sorry."

"I'm not angry," she said. "Don't think it. I'm just worried."

"You needn't be worried," I said.

"Why not? Aren't you worried? You're his friend."

"No, I'm not worried," I said. "I'm not worried, because I know what sort of pilot he is."

"Oh, you do, do you? Well, what sort of pilot is he?" she said. "He never tells me. He never talks about it at all."

"They never do," I said.

"Sometimes I think I'll never know what sort of person he is. Never!"

I felt there was little I could say to her. She was angry because I was the wrong person and because she was frustrated. I bought her several drinks. For a time she was quieter and then once more she got excited. "One night he'll get shot down and about all I'll know of him is that his name was Albert!"

"Take it easy," I said. "In the first place he won't get shot down."

"No? How are you so sure?"

"He's the sort that shoots other people down first."

"Are you trying to be funny?" she said.

"No," I said; and for a few minutes I tried to tell her why it was not funny and why I had spoken that way. I tried quite hard, but I do not think she understood. I realized that she knew nothing of all that had happened in Kalgoorlie—the blank year, the awful discovery about England, the bewilderment and the anger. I tried to make her see that there is a type who thinks of nothing but the idea that he may be shot at; and that there is another type, of which he was one, who thinks of nothing but shooting first. "He's glad to go. He wants to go. It's what he lives for," I said. "Don't you see?"

No sooner had I said it than I realized that it was the stupidest thing in the world to say. It was herself, not flying, that she wanted him to live for. She did not understand, and it would have sounded very silly if I had tried to tell her that he was engaged on something like a mission of vengeance; that because of all that had happened in Kalgoorlie, and especially that one day in Kalgoorlie, he felt that he had something cruel and hideous to wipe out from his conception of what was a decent life on earth. Every time he went up, something was vindicated. Nor did she understand, and again it might have sounded foolish too, that it was the living and positive clarity of the whole idea that was really his preservation. All I could say was, "He's the sort that goes on coming back and coming back until they're fed up with him and make him an instructor."

Nevertheless, that night her fears were almost justified. The flak over Bremen was very hostile, and it seemed that he had to take a lot of hasty evasive action before he could get clear away along the coast. They had brought him down even then to about two thousand feet. The searchlights were very thick too, and it was like daylight in the aircraft marking the time. But as if he couldn't possibly miss the opportunity, he came down to three hundred feet, roaring over the searchlight batteries as his gunners attacked them. They flew for about forty miles in this way, until finally something hit the outer starboard engine and holed the starboard wing. After that they were in a very bad way and got home, as he said, later than originally proposed.

I do not think he told her about this. It went down into his log, and some of it may have gone down into the diary he had promised faithfully to keep for his people back on the farm. He was satisfied that he had blown out about twenty searchlights, and that was all. Something else was vindicated. Two days later he had another go. In quite a short daylight attack along the Dutch coast he got into an argument with a flak ship. He was in a very positive mood and he decided to go down to attack. As he was coming in, his rear gunner sighted a formation of Messerschmitts coming up astern, and two minutes later they attacked him. He must have engaged them for about fifteen minutes. He had always hated Messerschmitts, and to be attacked by them made him very angry indeed. At the end of the engagement he had shot down two of them and had crippled a third, but they in turn had holed the aircraft in fifteen places. Nevertheless, he went down just to carry out his instruction of giving the flak ship a good-by kiss. She had ceased firing, and he went in almost to low level and just missed her with his last two bombs by the stern. As he was coming home his outer port engine gave up, but he tootled in just before darkness, quite happy. "A piece of cake," he said.

I know that he did not tell her about this either, and I could see that she had some excuse for thinking him undemonstrative and perhaps unheroic. For the next two days there was thick fog and rime frost in the early morning that covered the wings of the Stirlings with dusty silver. He was impatient because of the fog, and we played many games of cribbage in the mess on the second day while the crews were grounded.

On the third day he came back from briefing with a very satisfied look on his face. "A little visit to Mr. Salmin and

Mr. Gluckstein at Brest," he said. He had been flying just a year. He had done twenty trips, all of them with the same meaning. It was a bright calm day, without cloud, quite warm in the winter sun. There were pools of water here and there on the runways, and looking through the glasses I could see little brushy silver tails spurting up from the wheels of the aircraft as they taxied away.

When I looked into the air, again through the glasses, I saw two aircraft circling round, waiting to formate before setting course. One of them was smoking a little from the outer port engine. The smoking seemed to increase a little, and then became black. Suddenly it seemed as if the whole engine burst silently and softly into crimson flower. I kept looking through the glasses, transfixed, but suddenly the aircraft went away behind the hangars as it came down.

That evening I waited until it was quite dark before going into the town. I went into the bar of the Grenadier, and the girl was standing by the bar talking to the barmaid. She was drinking a port while waiting for him to come.

"Hello," she said. Her voice was cold, and I knew that she was disappointed.

"Hello. Could you come outside a moment?" I said.

She finished her port and came outside and we stood in the street, in the darkness. Some people went by, shining a torch on the dirty road, and in the light I could see the sleeves of her coat hanging loose, as if she had no arms. I waited until the people had gone by, and then, not knowing how to say it, I told her what had happened. "It wasn't very heroic," I said. "It was rotten luck. Just rotten luck, that's all."

I was afraid she would cry.

She stood still and quite silent. I felt that I had to do something to comfort her and I made as if to take hold of her arm, but I only caught the sleeve, which was dead and empty. I felt suddenly far away from her and as if we had known two different people—almost as if she had not known him at all.

"I'll take you to have a drink," I said.

"No."

"You'll feel better."

"Why did it have to happen?" she said suddenly, raising her voice. "Why did it have to happen?"

"It's the way it often does happen," I answered.

"Yes, it's the way it often does happen!" she said. "Is that all you care? Is that all anyone cares? It's the way it happens!"

I did not speak. For a moment I was not thinking of her. I was thinking of a young man in a barber's saloon in Kalgoorlie, about to make the shocking discovery that the world was at war and that he did not know it.

"Yes, it's the way it happens!" she said. I could not see her face in the darkness, but her voice was very bitter now. "In a week nobody will ever know he flew. He's just one of thousands who go up and never come back. I never knew him. Nobody ever knew him. In a week nobody will know him from anyone else. Nobody will even remember him."

For a moment I did not answer. Now I was not thinking of him. I was thinking of the two people who had so bravely and stupidly kept the war from him and then had so bravely and proudly let him go. I was thinking of the farm with the sheep and the eucalyptus trees, the pink and mauve asters and the yellow spring wattle flaming in the sun. I was thinking of the thousands of farms like it, peopled by thousands of people like them: the simple, decent, kindly, immemorial people all over the earth.

"No," I said to her. "There will be many who will remember him."

The Enemy

PEARL BUCK

Dr. Sadao Hoki's house was built on a spot of the Japanese coast where as a little boy he had often played. The low square stone house was set upon rocks well above a narrow beach that was outlined with bent pines. As a boy Sadao had climbed the pines, supporting himself on his bare feet, as he had seen men do in the South Seas when they climbed for coconuts. His father had taken him often to the islands of those seas, and never had he failed to say to the grave little boy at his side, "Those islands yonder, they are the steppingstones to the future for Japan."

"Where shall we step from them?" Sadao had asked seriously.

"Who knows?" his father had answered. "Who can limit our future? It depends on what we make it."

Sadao had taken this into his mind, as he did everything his father said, his father who never joked or played with him, but who spent infinite pains upon him who was his only son. Sadao knew that his education was his father's chief concern. For this reason he had been sent at twenty-two to America to learn all that could be learned of surgery and medicine. He had come back at thirty, and before his father died he had seen Sadao become famous not only as a surgeon but as a scientist. Because he was now perfecting a discovery which would render wounds entirely clean, he had not been sent abroad with the troops. Also, he knew, there was some slight danger that the old General might need an operation for a condition for which he was now being treated medically, and for this possibility Sadao was being kept in Japan.

Clouds were rising from the ocean now. The unexpected warmth of the past few days had at night drawn heavy fog from the cold waves. Sadao watched mists hide outlines of a little island near the shore and then come creeping up the beach below the house, wreathing around the pines. In a few minutes fog would be wrapped about the house too. Then he would go into the room where Hana, his wife, would be waiting for him with the two children.

But at this moment the door opened and she looked out, a dark blue woolen haori over her kimono. She came to him affectionately and put her arm through his as he stood, smiled, and said nothing. He had met Hana in America, but he had waited to fall in love with her until he was sure she was Japanese. His father would never have received her unless she had been pure in her race. He wondered often whom he would have married if he had not met Hana, and by what luck he had found her in the most casual way, by chance literally, at an American professor's house. The professor and his wife had been kind people, anxious to do something for their few foreign students, and the students, though bored, had accepted this kindness. Sadao had often told Hana how nearly he had not gone to Professor Harley's house that night—the rooms were so small, the food so bad, the professor's wife so voluble. But he had gone and there he had found Hana, a new student, and had felt he would love her if it were at all possible.

Now he felt her hand on his arm and was aware of the pleasure it gave him, even though they had been married years enough to have the two children. For they had not married heedlessly in America. They had finished their work at school and had come home to Japan, and when his father had seen her the marriage had been arranged in the old Japanese way, although Sadao and Hana had talked everything over beforehand. They were perfectly happy. She laid her cheek against his arm.

It was at this moment that both of them saw something black come out of the mists. It was a man. He was flung up out of the ocean—flung, it seemed, to his feet by a breaker.

He staggered a few steps, his body outlined against the mist, his arms above his head. Then the curled mists hid him again.

"Who is that?" Hana cried. She dropped Sadao's arm and they both leaned over the railing of the veranda. Now they saw him again. The man was on his hands and knees crawling. Then they saw him fall on his face and lie there.

"A fisherman perhaps," Sadao said, "washed from his boat." He ran quickly down the steps, and behind him Hana came, her wide sleeves flying. A mile or two away on either side there were fishing villages, but here was only the bare and lonely coast, dangerous with rocks. The surf beyond the beach was spiked with rocks. Somehow the man had managed to come through them—he must be badly torn.

They saw when they came toward him that indeed it was so. The sand on one side of him had already a stain of red soaking through.

"He is wounded," Sadao exclaimed. He made haste to the man, who lay motionless, his face in the sand. An old cap stuck to his head, soaked with sea water. He was in wet rags of garments. Sadao stooped, Hana at his side, and turned the man's head. They saw the face.

"A white man!" Hana whispered.

Yes, it was a white man. The wet cap fell away and there was his wet yellow hair, long, as though for many weeks it had not been cut, and upon his young and tortured face was a rough yellow beard. He was unconscious and knew nothing that they did to him.

Now Sadao remembered the wound, and with his expert fingers he began to search for it. Blood flowed freshly at his touch. On the right side of his lower back Sadao saw that a gun wound had been reopened. The flesh was blackened with powder. Sometime, not many days ago, the man had been shot and had not been tended. It was bad chance that the rock had struck the wound.

"Oh, how he is bleeding!" Hana whispered again in a solemn voice. The mists screened them now completely, and at this time of day no one came by. The fishermen had gone home, and even the chance beachcombers would have considered the day at an end.

"What shall we do with this man?" Sadao muttered. But his trained hands seemed of their own will to be doing what they could to stanch the fearful bleeding. He packed the wound with the sea moss that strewed the beach. The man moaned with pain in his stupor, but he did not awaken.

"The best thing that we could do would be to put him back in the sea," Sadao said, answering himself.

Now that the bleeding was stopped for the moment he stood up and dusted the sand from his hands.

"Yes, undoubtedly, that would be best," Hana said steadily. But she continued to stare down at the motionless man.

"If we sheltered a white man in our house we should be arrested, and if we turned him over as a prisoner, he would certainly die," Sadao said.

"The kindest thing would be to put him back into the sea," Hana said. But neither of them moved. They were staring with a curious repulsion upon the inert figure.

"What is he?" Hana whispered.

"There is something about him that looks American," Sadao said. He took up the battered cap. Yes, there, almost gone, was the faint lettering. "A sailor," he said, "from an American warship." He spelled it out: "U.S. Navy." The man was a prisoner of war!

"He has escaped," Hana cried softly, "and that is why he is wounded."

"In the back," Sadao agreed.

They hesitated, looking at each other. Then Hana said with resolution, "Come, are we able to put him back into the sea?"

"If I am able, are you?" Sadao asked.

"No," Hana said. "But if you can do it alone. . . ."

Sadao hesitated again. "The strange thing is," he said, "that if the man were whole I could turn him over to the police without difficulty. I care nothing for him. He is my enemy. All Americans are my enemy. And he is only a common fellow. You see how foolish his face is. But since he is wounded. . . ."

"You also cannot throw him back to the sea," Hana said. "Then there is only one thing to do. We must carry him into the house."

"But the servants?" Sadao inquired.

"We must simply tell them that we intend to give him to the police—as indeed we must, Sadao. We must think of the children and your position. It would endanger all of us if we did not give this man over as a prisoner of war."

"Certainly," Sadao agreed. "I would not think of doing anything else."

Thus agreed, together they lifted the man. He was very light, like a fowl that has been half-starved for a long time until it is only feathers and skeleton. So, his arms hanging, they carried him up the steps and into the side door of the house. This door opened into a passage, and down the passage they carried the man toward an empty bedroom. It had been the bedroom of Sadao's father and since his death it had not been used. They laid the man on the deeply matted floor. Everything here had been Japanese to please the old man, who would never in his own home sit on a chair or sleep in a foreign bed. Hana went to the wall cupboards and slid back a door and took out a soft quilt. She hesitated. The quilt was covered with flowered silk and the lining was pure white silk.

"He is so dirty," she murmured in distress.

"Yes, he had better be washed," Sadao agreed. "If you will fetch hot water I will wash him."

"I cannot bear to have you touch him," she said. "We shall have to tell the servants he is here. I will tell Yumi now. She can leave the children for a few minutes and she can wash him."

Sadao considered a moment. "Let it be so," he agreed. "You tell Yumi and I will tell the others."

But the utter pallor of the man's unconscious face moved him first to stoop and feel his pulse. It was faint, but it was there. He put his hand against the man's cold breast. The heart too was yet alive.

"He will die unless he is operated on," Sadao said, considering. "The question is whether he will not die anyway."

Hana cried out in fear. "Don't try to save him! What if he should live?"

"What if he should die?" Sadao replied. He stood gazing down on the motionless man. This man must have extraordinary vitality or he would have been dead by now. But then he was very young—perhaps not yet twenty-five.

"You mean die from the operation?" Hana asked.

"Yes," Sadao said.

Hana considered this doubtfully, and when she did not answer Sadao turned away. "At any rate something must be done with him," he said, "and first he must be washed." He went quickly out of the room and Hana came behind him. She did not wish to be left alone with the white man. He was the first she had seen since she left America, and now he seemed to have nothing to do with those whom she had known there. Here he was her enemy, a menace, living or dead.

She turned to the nursery and called, "Yumi!"

But the children heard her voice and she had to go in for a moment and smile at them and play with the baby boy, now nearly three months old.

Over the baby's soft black hair she motioned with her mouth, "Yumi—come with me!"

"I will put the baby to bed," Yumi replied. "He is ready."

She went with Yumi into the bedroom next to the nursery and stood with the boy in her arms while Yumi spread the sleeping quilts on the floor and laid the baby between them.

Then Hana led the way quickly and softly to the kitchen. The two servants were frightened at what their master had just told them. The old gardener, who was also a house servant, pulled the few hairs on his upper lip.

"The master ought not to heal the wound of this white man," he said bluntly to Hana. "The white man ought to die. First he was shot. Then the sea caught him and wounded him with her rocks. If the master heals what the gun did and what the sea did they will take revenge on us."

"I will tell him what you say," Hana replied courteously. But she herself was also frightened, although she was not superstitious as the old man was. Could it ever be well to help an enemy? Nevertheless, she told Yumi to fetch the hot water and bring it to the room where the white man was.

She went ahead and slid back the partitions. Sadao was not yet there. Yumi, following, put down her wooden bucket. Then she went over to the white man. When she saw him her thick lips folded themselves into stubbornness. "I have never washed a white man," she said, "and I will not wash so dirty a one now."

Hana cried at her severely, "You will do what your master commands you!"

"My master ought not to command me to wash the enemy," Yumi said stubbornly.

There was so fierce a look of resistance upon Yumi's round dull face that Hana felt unreasonably afraid. After all, if the servants should report something that was not as it happened?

"Very well," she said with dignity. "You understand we only want to bring him to his senses so that we can turn him over as a prisoner?"

"I will have nothing to do with it," Yumi said. "I am a poor person and it is not my business."

"Then please," Hana said gently, "return to your own work."

At once Yumi left the room. But this left Hana with the

white man alone. She might have been too afraid to stay had not her anger at Yumi's stubbornness now sustained her.

"Stupid Yumi," she muttered fiercely. "Is this anything but a man? And a wounded, helpless man!"

In the conviction of her own superiority she bent impulsively and untied the knotted rags that kept the white man covered. When she had his breast bare she dipped the small clean towel that Yumi had brought into the steaming hot water and washed his face carefully. The man's skin, though rough with exposure, was of a fine texture and must have been very blond when he was a child.

While she was thinking these thoughts, though not really liking the man better now that he was no longer a child, she kept on washing him until his upper body was quite clean. But she dared not turn him over. Where was Sadao? Now her anger was ebbing and she was anxious again, and she rose, wiping her hands on the wrung towel. Then lest the man be chilled she put the quilt over him.

"Sadao!" she called softly.

He had been about to come in when she called. His hand had been on the door and now he opened it. She saw that he had brought his surgeon's emergency bag and that he wore his surgeon's coat.

"You have decided to operate!" she cried.

"Yes," he said shortly. He turned his back to her and unfolded a sterilized towel upon the floor of the *takonoma* alcove, and put his instruments out upon it.

"Fetch towels," he said.

She went obediently, but how anxious now, to the linen

shelves and took out the towels. There ought also to be old pieces of matting so that the blood would not ruin the fine floor covering. She went out to the back veranda where the gardener kept strips of matting with which to protect delicate shrubs on cold nights and took an armful of them.

But when she went back into the room she saw this was useless. The blood had already soaked through the packing in the man's wound and had ruined the mat under him.

"Oh, the mat!" she cried.

"Yes, it is ruined," Sadao replied, as though he did not care. "Help me to turn him," he commanded her.

She obeyed him without a word, and he began to wash the man's back carefully.

"Yumi would not wash him," she said.

"Did you wash him, then?" Sadao asked, not stopping for a moment his swift concise movements.

"Yes," she said.

He did not seem to hear her. But she was used to his absorption when he was at work. She wondered for a moment if it mattered to him what was the body upon which he worked, so long as it was for the work he did so excellently.

"You will have to give the anesthetic if he needs it," he said.

"I?" she repeated blankly. "But never have I!"

"It is easy enough," he said impatiently.

He was taking out the packing now and the blood began to flow more quickly. He peered into the wound with the bright surgeon's light fastened on his forehead. "The bullet is still there," he said with cool interest. "Now I wonder how deep this rock wound is. If it is not too deep it may be that

I can get the bullet. But the bleeding is not superficial. He has lost much blood."

At this moment Hana choked. He looked up and saw her face the color of sulphur.

"Don't faint," he said sharply. He did not put down his exploring instrument. "If I stop now the man will surely die." She clapped her hands to her mouth and leaped up and ran out of the room. Outside in the garden he heard her retching. But he went on with his work.

It will be better for her to empty her stomach, he thought. He had forgotten that of course she had never seen an operation. But her distress and his inability to go to her at once made him impatient and irritable with this man who lay like dead under his knife.

This man, he thought, there is no reason under heaven why he should live.

Unconsciously this thought made him ruthless and he proceeded swiftly. In his dream the man moaned, but Sadao paid no heed except to mutter at him.

"Groan," he muttered, "groan if you like. I am not doing this for my own pleasure. In fact, I do not know why I am doing it."

The door opened and there was Hana again. She had not stopped even to smooth back her hair.

"Where is the anesthetic?" she asked in a clear voice.

Sadao motioned with his chin. "It is as well that you came back," he said. "This fellow is beginning to stir."

She had the bottle and some cotton in her hand.

"But how shall I do it?" she asked.

"Simply saturate the cotton and hold it near his nostrils,"

Sadao replied without delaying for one moment the intricate detail of his work. "When he breathes badly, move it away a little."

She crouched close to the sleeping face of the young American. It was a piteously thin face, she thought, and the lips were twisted. The man was suffering whether he knew it or not. Watching him, she wondered if the stories they heard sometimes of the sufferings of prisoners were true. They came like flickers of rumor, told by word of mouth and always contradicted. In the newspapers the reports were always that wherever the Japanese armies went the people received them gladly, with cries of joy at their liberation. But sometimes she remembered such men as General Takima, who at home beat his wife cruelly, though no one mentioned it now that he had fought so victorious a battle in Manchuria. If a man like that could be so cruel to a woman in his power, would he not be cruel to one like this for instance?

She hoped anxiously that this young man had not been tortured. It was at this moment that she observed deep red scars on his neck, just under the ear. "Those scars," she murmured, lifting her eyes to Sadao.

But he did not answer. At this moment he felt the tip of his instrument strike against something hard, dangerously near the kidney. All thought left him. He felt only the purest pleasure. He probed with his fingers, delicately, familiar with every atom of this human body. His old American professor of anatomy had seen to that knowledge. "Ignorance of the human body is the surgeon's cardinal sin, sirs!" he had thundered at his classes year after year. "To operate without as complete knowledge of the body as if you had made it—anything less than that is murder."

"It is not quite at the kidney, my friend," Sadao murmured. It was his habit to murmur to the patient when he forgot himself in an operation. "My friend," he always called his patients and so now he did, forgetting that this was his enemy.

Then quickly, with the cleanest and most precise of incisions, the bullet was out. The man quivered, but he was still unconscious. Nevertheless, he muttered a few English words.

"Guts," he muttered, choking. "They got . . . my guts. . . ."

"Sadao!" Hana cried sharply.

"Hush," Sadao said.

The man sank again into silence so profound that Sadao took up his wrist, hating the touch of it. Yes, there was still a pulse so faint, so feeble, but enough, if he wanted the man to live, to give hope.

But certainly I do not want this man to live, he thought with bitterness.

"No more anesthetic," he told Hana.

He turned as swiftly as though he had never paused, and from his medicines he chose a small vial and from it filled a hypodermic and thrust it into the patient's left arm. Then, putting down the needle, he took the man's wrist again. The pulse under his fingers fluttered once or twice and then grew stronger.

"This man will live in spite of all," he said to Hana, and sighed.

The young man woke, so weak, his blue eyes so terrified when he perceived where he was, that Hana felt compelled to apology. She served him herself, for none of the servants would enter the room.

When she came in the first time she saw him summon his small strength to be prepared for some fearful thing.

"Don't be afraid," she begged him softly.

"How come . . . you speak English?" he gasped.

"I was a long time in America," she replied.

She saw that he wanted to reply to that, but he could not, and so she knelt and fed him gently from the porcelain spoon. He ate unwillingly, but still he ate.

"Now you will soon be strong," she said, not liking him and yet moved to comfort him.

He did not answer.

When Sadao came in the third day after the operation he found the young man sitting up, his face bloodless with the effort.

"Lie down," Sadao cried. "Do you want to die?"

He forced the man down gently and strongly and examined the wound. "You may kill yourself if you do this sort of thing," he scolded.

"What are you going to do with me?" the boy muttered. He looked just now barely seventeen. "Are you going to hand me over?"

For a moment Sadao did not answer. He finished his examination and then pulled the silk quilt over the man. "I do not know myself what I shall do with you," he said. "I ought, of course, to give you to the police. You are a prisoner of war—no, do not tell me anything." He put up his hand as he saw the young man about to speak. "Do not even tell me your name unless I ask it."

They looked at each other for a moment, and then the young man closed his eyes and turned his face to the wall. "Okay," he whispered, his mouth a bitter line.

Outside the door Hana was waiting for Sadao. He saw at once that she was in trouble.

"Sadao, Yumi tells me the servants feel they cannot stay if we hide this man here any more," she said. "She tells me that they are saying that you and I were so long in America that we have forgotten to think of our own country first. They think we like Americans."

"It is not true," Sadao said harshly. "Americans are our enemies. But I have been trained not to let a man die if I can help it."

"The servants cannot understand that," she said.

"No," he agreed.

Neither seemed able to say more, and somehow the household dragged on. The servants grew daily more watchful. Their courtesy was as careful as ever, but their eyes were cold upon the pair by whom they were hired.

"It is clear what our master ought to do," the old gardener said one morning. He had worked with flowers all his life, and had been a specialist too in moss. For Sadao's father he had made one of the finest moss gardens in Japan, sweeping the bright green carpet constantly so that not a leaf or a pine needle marred the velvet of its surface. "My old master's son knows very well what he ought to do," he now said, pinching a bud from a bush as he spoke. "When the man was so near death why did he not let him bleed?"

"That young master is so proud of his skill to save life that he saves any life," the cook said contemptuously. She split a fowl's neck skillfully and held the fluttering bird and let its blood flow into the roots of a wistaria vine. Blood is the best of fertilizers, and the old gardener would not let her waste a drop of it.

"It is the children of whom we must think," Yumi said sadly. "What will be their fate if their father is condemned as a traitor?"

They did not try to hide what they said from the ears of Hana as she stood arranging the day's flowers in the veranda near by, and she knew they spoke on purpose that she might hear. That they were right she knew too in most of her being. But there was another part of her, which she herself could not understand. It was not sentimental liking of the prisoner. She had not liked him even yesterday when he had said in his impulsive way, "Anyway, let me tell you that my name is Tom." She had only bowed her little distant bow. She saw hurt in his eyes, but she did not wish to assuage it. Indeed, he was a great trouble in this house.

As for Sadao, every day he examined the wound carefully. The last stitches had been pulled out this morning, and the young man would in a fortnight be nearly as well as ever. Sadao went back to his office and carefully typed a letter to the chief of police reporting the whole matter. "On the twenty-first day of February an escaped prisoner was washed up on the shore in front of my house." So far he typed, and then he opened a secret drawer of his desk and put the unfinished report into it.

On the seventh day after that two things happened. In

the morning the servants left together, their belongings tied in large square cotton kerchiefs. When Hana got up in the morning nothing was done, the house not cleaned and the food not prepared, and she knew what it meant. She was dismayed and even terrified, but her pride as a mistress would not allow her to show it. Instead she inclined her head gracefully when they appeared before her in the kitchen, and she paid them off and thanked them for all that they had done for her. They were crying, but she did not cry. The cook and the gardener had served Sadao since he was a little boy in his father's house, and Yumi cried because of the children. She was so grieving that after she had gone she ran back to Hana.

"If the baby misses me too much tonight, send for me. I am going to my own house and you know where it is."

"Thank you," Hana said, smiling. But she told herself she would not send for Yumi however the baby cried.

She made the breakfast and Sadao helped with the children. Neither of them spoke of the servants beyond the fact that they were gone. But after Hana had taken morning food to the prisoner she came back to Sadao.

"Why is it we cannot see clearly what we ought to do?" she asked him. "Even the servants see more clearly than we do. Why are we different from other Japanese?"

Sadao did not answer. But a little later he went into the room where the prisoner was and said brusquely, "Today you may get up on your feet. I want you to stay up only five minutes at a time. Tomorrow you may try it twice as long. It would be well that you get back your strength as quickly as possible."

He saw the flicker of terror on the young face that was still very pale.

"Okay," the boy murmured. Evidently he was determined to say more. "I feel I ought to thank you, Doctor, for having saved my life."

"Don't thank me too early," Sadao said coldly. He saw the flicker of terror again in the boy's eyes—terror as unmistakable as an animal's. The scars on his neck were crimson for a moment. Those scars! What were they? Sadao did not ask.

In the afternoon the second thing happened. Hana, working hard at unaccustomed labor, saw a messenger come to the door in official uniform. Her hands went weak and she could not draw her breath. The servants must have told already. She ran to Sadao, gasping, unable to utter a word. But by then the messenger had simply followed her through the garden and there he stood. She pointed at him helplessly.

Sadao looked up from his book. He was in his office, the outer partition of which was thrown open to the garden for the southern sunshine.

"What is it?" he asked the messenger, and then he rose, seeing the man's uniform.

"You are to come to the palace," the man said. "The old General is in pain again."

"Oh," Hana breathed, "is that all?"

"All!" the messenger exclaimed. "Is it not enough?"

"Indeed it is," she replied. "I am very sorry."

When Sadao came to say good-by she was in the kitchen, but doing nothing. The children were asleep and she sat merely resting for a moment, more exhausted from her fright than from work.

"I thought they had come to arrest you," she said.

He gazed down into her anxious eyes. "I must get rid of this man for your sake," he said in distress. "Somehow I must get rid of him."

"Of course," the General said weakly, "I understand fully. But that is because I once took a degree in Princeton. So few Japanese have."

"I care nothing for the man, Excellency," Sadao said, "but having operated on him with such success. . . ."

"Yes, yes," the General said. "It only makes me feel you more indispensable to me. Evidently you can save anyone —you are so skilled. You say you think I can stand one more such attack as I have had today?"

"Not more than one," Sadao said.

"Then certainly I can allow nothing to happen to you," the General said with anxiety. His long, pale, Japanese face became expressionless, which meant that he was in deep thought. "You cannot be arrested," the General said, closing his eyes. "Suppose you were condemned to death and the next day I had to have my operation?"

"There are other surgeons, Excellency," Sadao suggested.

"None I trust," the General replied. "The best ones have been trained by Germans and would consider the operation successful even if I died. I do not care for their point of view." He sighed. "It seems a pity that we cannot better combine the German ruthlessness with the American sentimentality. Then you could turn your prisoner over to execution and yet I could be sure you would not murder me while I was unconscious." The General laughed. He had an unusual sense of humor. "As a Japanese, could you not combine these two foreign elements?" he asked.

Sadao smiled. "I am not quite sure," he said, "but for your sake I would be willing to try, Excellency."

The General shook his head. "I had rather not be the test case," he said. He felt suddenly weak and overwhelmed with the cares of his life as an official in times such as these, when repeated victory brought great responsibilities all over the south Pacific. "It is very unfortunate that this man should have washed up on your doorstep," he said irritably.

"I feel it so myself," Sadao said gently.

"It would be best if he could be quietly killed," the General said. "Not by you, but by someone who does not know him. I have my own private assassins. Suppose I send two of them to your house tonight—or better, any night. You need know nothing about it. It is now warm—what would be more natural than that you should leave the outer partition of the white man's room open to the garden while he sleeps?"

"Certainly it would be very natural," Sadao agreed. "In fact, it is so left open every night."

"Good," the General said, yawning. "They are very capable assassins—they make no noise and they know the trick of inward bleeding. If you like I can even have them remove the body."

Sadao considered. "That perhaps would be best, Excellency," he agreed, thinking of Hana.

He left the General's presence then and went home,

thinking over the plan. In this way the whole thing would be taken out of his hands. He would tell Hana nothing, since she would be timid at the idea of assassins in the house, and yet certainly such persons were essential in an absolute state such as Japan was. How else could rulers deal with those who opposed them?

He refused to allow anything but reason to be the atmosphere of his mind as he went into the room where the American was in bed. But as he opened the door, to his surprise he found the young man out of bed, and preparing to go into the garden.

"What is this!" he exclaimed. "Who gave you permission to leave your room?"

"I'm not used to waiting for permission," Tom said gaily. "Gosh, I feel pretty good again! But will the muscles on this side always feel stiff?"

"Is it so?" Sadao inquired, surprised. He forgot all else. "Now I thought I had provided against that," he murmured. He lifted the edge of the man's shirt and gazed at the healing scar. "Massage may do it," he said, "if exercise does not."

"It won't bother me much," the young man said. His young face was gaunt under the stubbly blond beard. "Say, Doctor, I've got something I want to say to you. If I hadn't met a Jap like you—well, I wouldn't be alive today. I know that."

Sadao bowed but he could not speak.

"Sure, I know that," Tom went on warmly. His big thin hands, gripping a chair, were white at the knuckles. "I guess if all the Japs were like you there wouldn't have been a war."

"Perhaps," Sadao said with difficulty. "And now I think you had better go back to bed."

Sadao slept badly that night. Time and time again he woke, thinking he heard the rustling of footsteps, the sound of a twig broken or a stone displaced in the garden—a noise such as men might make who carried a burden.

The next morning he made the excuse to go first into the guest room. If the American were gone, he then could simply tell Hana that so the General had directed. But when he opened the door he saw at once that it was not last night. There on the pillow was the shaggy blond head. He could hear the peaceful breathing of sleep, and he closed the door again quietly.

"He is asleep," he told Hana. "He is almost well to sleep like that."

"What shall we do with him?" Hana whispered her old refrain.

Sadao shook his head. "I must decide in a day or two," he promised.

But certainly, he thought, the second night must be the night. There rose a wind that night, and he listened to the sounds of bending boughs and whistling partitions.

Hana woke too. "Ought we not to go and close the sick man's partition?" she asked.

"No," Sadao said. "He is able now to do it for himself."

But the next morning the American was still there.

Then the third night of course must be the night. The wind changed to quiet rain and the garden was full of the sound of dripping eaves and running springs. Sadao slept a little better, but he woke at the sound of a crash and leaped to his feet.

"What was that?" Hana cried. The baby woke at her voice and began to wail. "I must go and see."

But he held her and would not let her move.

"Sadao," she cried, "what is the matter with you?"

"Don't go," he muttered, "don't go!"

His terror infected her and she stood breathless, waiting. There was only silence. Together they crept back into the bed, the baby between them.

Yet when he opened the door of the guest room in the morning, there was the young man. He was very gay and had already washed and was now on his feet. He had asked for a razor yesterday and had shaved himself, and there was faint color in his cheeks. "I am well," he said joyously.

Sadao drew his kimono around his weary body. He could not, he decided suddenly, go through another night. It was not that he cared for this young man's life. No, simply it was not worth the strain.

"You are well," Sadao agreed. He lowered his voice. "You are so well that I think if I put my boat on the shore tonight, with food and extra clothing in it, you might be able to row to that little island not far from the coast. It is so near the coast that it has not been worth fortifying. Nobody lives on it because in storm it is submerged. But this is not the season of storm. You could live there until you saw a Korean fishing boat pass by. They pass quite near the island because the water is many fathoms deep there."

The young man stared at him, slowly comprehending. "Do I have to?" he asked.

"I think so," Sadao said gently. "You understand—it is not hidden that you are here."

The young man nodded in perfect comprehension. "Okay," he said simply.

Sadao did not see him again until evening. As soon as it was dark he had dragged the stout boat down to the shore, and in it he put food and bottled water that he had bought secretly during the day, as well as two quilts he had bought at a pawnshop. The boat he tied to a post in the water, for the tide was high. There was no moon and he worked without a flashlight.

When he came to the house he entered as though he were just back from his work, and so Hana knew nothing. "Yumi was here today," she said as she served his supper. Though she was so modern, still she did not eat with him. "Yumi cried over the baby," she went on with a sigh. "She misses him so."

"The servants will come back as soon as the foreigner is gone," Sadao said.

He went into the guest room that night before he went to bed and himself checked carefully the American's temperature, the state of the wound, and his heart and pulse. The pulse was irregular, but that was perhaps because of excitement. The young man's pale lips were pressed together and his eyes burned. Only the scars on his neck were red.

"I realize you are saving my life again," he told Sadao.

"Not at all," Sadao said. "It is only inconvenient to have you here any longer."

He had hesitated a good deal about giving the man a flashlight. But he had decided to give it to him after all. It was a small one, his own, which he used at night when he was called.

"If your food runs out before you catch a boat," he said, "signal me two flashes at the same instant the sun drops over the horizon. Do not signal in darkness, for it will be seen. If you are all right, but still there, signal me once. You will find fish easy to catch, but you must eat them raw. A fire would be seen."

"Okay," the young man breathed.

He was dressed now in the Japanese clothes that Sadao had given him, and at the last moment Sadao wrapped a black cloth about his blond head.

"Now," Sadao said.

The young American without a word shook Sadao's hand warmly and then walked quite well across the floor and down the step into the darkness of the garden. Once—twice—Sadao saw his light flash to find his way. But that would not be suspected. He waited until from the shore there was one more flash. Then he closed the partition. That night he slept.

"You say the man escaped?" the General asked faintly. He had been operated upon a week before, an emergency operation to which Sadao had been called in the night. For twelve hours Sadao had not been sure the General would live. The gall bladder was much involved. Then the old man had begun to breathe deeply again and to demand food. Sadao had not been able to ask about the assassins. So far as he knew they had never come. The servants had returned, and Yumi had cleaned the guest room thoroughly and had burned sulphur in it to get the white man's smell out of it. Nobody said anything. Only the gardener was cross, because he had got behind with his chrysanthemums.

But after a week Sadao felt the General was well enough to be spoken to about the prisoner.

"Yes, Excellency, he escaped," Sadao now said. He coughed, signifying that he had not said all he might have said but was unwilling to disturb the General further. But the old man opened his eyes suddenly.

"That prisoner," he said with some energy, "did I not promise you I would kill him for you?"

"You did, Excellency," Sadao said.

"Well, well!" the old man said in a tone of amazement. "So I did! But you see, I was suffering a good deal. The truth is, I thought of nothing but myself. In short, I forgot my promise to you."

"I wondered, Your Excellency," Sadao murmured.

"It was certainly very careless of me," the General said. "But you understand it was not lack of patriotism or dereliction of duty." He looked anxiously at his doctor. "If the matter should come out, you would understand that, wouldn't you?"

"Certainly, Your Excellency," Sadao said. He suddenly comprehended that the General was in the palm of his hand and that as a consequence he himself was perfectly safe. "I can swear to your loyalty, Excellency," he said to the old General, "and to your zeal against the enemy."

"You are a good man," the General murmured, and closed his eyes. "You will be rewarded."

But Sadao, searching the spot of black in the twilighted

sea that night, had his reward. There was no prick of light in the dusk. No one was on the island. His prisoner was gone —safe, doubtless, for he had warned him to wait only for a Korean fishing boat.

He stood for a moment on the veranda, gazing out to the sea from whence the young man had come that other night. And into his mind, although without reason, there came other white faces he had known—the professor at whose house he had met Hana, a dull man, and his wife had been a silly, talkative woman, in spite of her wish to be kind. He remembered his old teacher of anatomy, who had been so insistent on mercy with the knife, and then he remembered the face of his fat and slatternly landlady. He had had great difficulty in finding a place to live in America, because he was a Japanese. The Americans were full of prejudice and it had been bitter to live in it, knowing himself their superior. How he had despised the ignorant and dirty old woman who had at last consented to house him in her miserable home! He had once tried to be grateful to her because she had in his last year nursed him through influenza, but it was difficult, for she was no less repulsive to him in her kindness. But then, white people were repulsive, of course. It was a relief to be openly at war with them at last. Now he remembered the youthful, haggard face of his prisoner—white and repulsive.

Strange, he thought, I wonder why I could not kill him?